Practical
CONSERVATION
WOODLANDS

By Andrew Lane and Joyce Tait

The Open University in association with the
Nature Conservancy Council

Hodder & Stoughton

LON   TO

CONSERVATION

Open University course team

Joyce Tait (Course Team Chair)

Andrew Lane (Lecturer)

Graham Turner (BBC Producer)

Susan Carr (Course Manager)

Amanda Smith (Editor)

Lesley Passey (Designer)

Roy Lawrance (Graphic Artist)

Ray Munns (Cartographer)

Julie Lane (Research Assistant)

Sue Snelling (Secretary)

Angela Walters (Secretary)

ISBN 0 340 53366 8

First published 1990

Typeset by Wearside Tradespools, Fulwell, Sunderland
Printed in Great Britain for the educational division of Hodder and Stoughton Ltd,
Mill Road, Dunton Green, Sevenoaks, Kent
by M. & A. Thomson Litho Limited, East Kilbride, Scotland

Contents

This book is produced by The Open University as part of the *Practical Conservation* training programme which deals with all aspects of conservation on land that is managed largely for commercial or recreational purposes (see Figure 0.1).

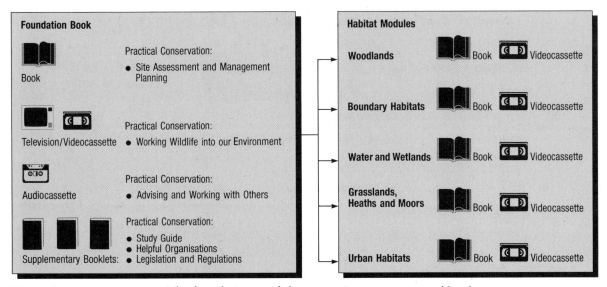

Figure 0.1
The Open University teaching programme for Practical Conservation

The foundation module covers site assessment and land use management planning in general and includes:

▶ the foundation book;

▶ a video cassette of a 50 minute television programme;

▶ a 60 minute audio cassette;

▶ two supplementary booklets;

▶ a *Study Guide* to the full programme.

This book with its accompanying 30 minute video cassette forms one of a series of modules on practical aspects of conservation management for a range of habitats:

▶ Woodlands;

▶ Boundary Habitats;

▶ Water and Wetlands;

▶ Grasslands, Heaths and Moors;

▶ Urban Habitats.

These training materials are suitable for use by groups or by individuals, studying alone or in association with a formal course. For those who would like to gain practical experience or a qualification, the Open University training programme is being incorporated into courses offered by colleges, field centres and other training bodies.

For further information please write to: Learning Materials Service Office, The Open University, PO Box 188, Walton Hall, Milton Keynes MK7 6DH.

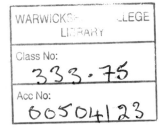

Chapter 1

INTRODUCTION

Woodland and forests of one kind or another cover about 10% of Britain and have a noticeable effect on the countryside. They can provide a good habitat for many species of wildlife and game and create landscape diversity, at the same time giving an income to the land holder or manager.

The conservation and commercial value of woodland both depend on which tree species are present and on how they have been managed in the past. However, the priorities for commercial management and for conservation can conflict, particularly when the woodland manager is not aware of their interactions. This book is a practical guide on how to integrate wildlife and landscape conservation with woodland and forestry management for commercial, recreational or game purposes, to provide the best possible outcome for all these interests. It should be used by all those who have, or would like to have, an active involvement in managing the countryside or other areas with conservation potential, including farmers, foresters, advisers, consultants, students, conservation volunteers, countryside rangers and park wardens, some school teachers and interested members of the general public.

Much of the woodland in this country has either lacked management in the long term, often leading to a decline in its value for conservation and for timber, or has been managed exclusively for commercial purposes, with little or no consideration for wildlife. Recent natural hazards, such as the spread of Dutch elm disease and destructive gales, have also greatly damaged some areas, although affected woods have an enormous capacity to recover in the long term. There are therefore tremendous opportunities now to improve on past performance, while maintaining the best existing woodland, and also to plant new areas of woodland, encouraged by more favourable government policies.

1.1   Woodland management

Most woodland in this country has been managed or influenced by human activities in the past, and it still needs to be managed to maintain or develop the characteristics we value, such as its contribution to the landscape, the wealth of wildlife it supports and the recreational enjoyment it provides. Increasingly, as for all forms of land use, this means producing a management plan to assess and determine the best management options. This also helps to cope with the complexity of running a modern business and to maintain continuity and consistency for long-term operations such as conservation and forestry.

Management planning in general is dealt with in the foundation module. The five main stages in the development of a plan are summarised again here in Figure 1.1. Stage 1 integrates landscape and wildlife conservation assessment with a consideration of the business aspects of land use, e.g. timber production, game rearing, recreation; Stage 2 identifies the land manager's objectives and the relevant constraints; Stage 3 involves exploring and

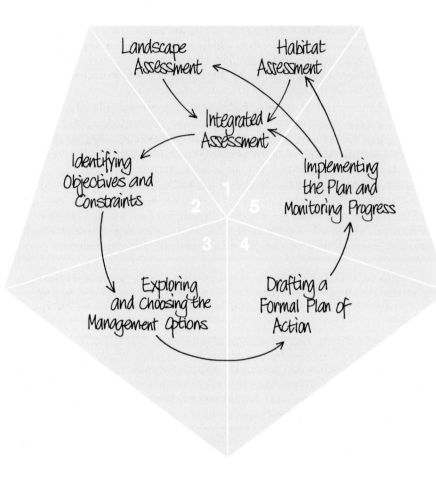

Figure 1.1 The process of land use management planning

choosing the options for achieving the objectives identified; in Stage 4 a formal plan of action is drafted; and Stage 5 puts the plan into practice and monitors progress.

Usually you should develop a general management plan for any area of land before going on to consider the place of woodland within it. This becomes particularly important if you are thinking of planting a new area of woodland. Under these circumstances you first need to answer the question 'Is woodland an appropriate use of this site?' If the site is already valuable for wildlife, for example as wetland, heathland, or herb-rich grassland, planting trees on it would result in a net conservation loss. The site may not be suitable for growing the tree species you would like to plant, or perhaps the trees would hide a beautiful view. You also need to consider how the long-term management of an area of woodland can be fitted in with any other business objectives. For any new plantation, you should only proceed if the general management plan indicates that, *all things considered*, it is the best use of the land.

This book and the associated video cassette concentrate on three particular aspects of management planning – assessment (Stage 1), management options

(Stage 3) and implementation (Stage 5). If you are preparing a management plan, or if you already have one, they will help you to put it into practice. Even if you do not want to become involved in management planning, they will help you to assess the present conservation value of woodland, to decide what can be done to maintain or improve it, to choose good sites and species mixtures for the creation of new woodland, and to put these ideas into practice.

A very important aspect of management planning is to recognise the importance of the manager's preferences. Any plan that goes against the manager's natural inclinations will not be given the long-term commitment needed to put it into practice. If you are an adviser or consultant, understanding the prejudices, interests, likes and dislikes of your client(s) will be an important part of your job. Even if you are a land manager yourself, and more or less in control of the situation, you may need to give this some careful thought, for example before deciding how to react to advice you are given or how to respond to new opportunities to invest in woodland planting or maintenance.

Attitudes to woodland

Those who are enthusiastic about woodland, whether from a conservation or commercial point of view, may be just as capable of doing damage through ill-considered action despite their good intentions as those who are indifferent towards it.

Felling large areas, planting large areas with monocultures of non-native species or planting oak trees in valuable herb-rich grassland would all be damaging from a conservation point of view. On the other hand, even those who have little time to give to woodland management can do a great deal of good by concentrating on the woodland edge and rides or glades within the wood and by planting small copses.

The important thing is to understand what you are doing and why, and to bear in mind the following simple guidelines:

Positive guidelines

- think before you act;
- first assess your area for its conservation and commercial value;
- consider as many options as possible;
- draw up a management plan, however brief;
- monitor changes in the area, good and bad;
- be prepared to change your plans.

1.2 The background to woodland management in Great Britain

The healthy forest presents an ever-changing scene – bare litter, thickets, open glades and dense stands, all with their attendant range of flora and fauna, subtly changing and interacting between the stages.

Sensitive woodland and forest planting has been carried out by traditional land owners for many centuries, and excellent examples can be seen in most parts of the country. Less easy to see are the changes which have taken place in the forest structure over the years; for example, some of the beech woodlands of the Cotswolds were established along with Scots pine and larch, which were subsequently removed for estate building purposes, when their role as protective trees ceased, or disappeared because of their shorter lifespan.

In mixed woodlands, old records show that often the finer specimens of oak, ash, elm, Scots pine and larch were removed, usually to pay death duties. The remaining woods, whilst chiefly broad-leaved in appearance and sometimes impressive by today's standards, by no means reflect their past status.

This country has not always had a national forest policy and large-scale plantings and fellings have often resulted from national emergencies such as the Second World War. This, together with fiscal problems such as death duties, has resulted in over cutting and the associated imbalance in the age and species structure of our woodlands.

Changing public opinion has helped encourage a broadening of forestry objectives. This is reflected in new grants aimed at greater diversification of woodland type and structure, providing a welcome opportunity to create more carefully balanced woodlands. Fashion should be viewed with suspicion in silviculture, but the return to a more harmonious and natural state deserves our full support.

This book is an introductory guide to woodland management and its interaction with wildlife and landscape conservation. It is a reminder to foresters not to neglect the ecological aspects and the valid interests of others and a guide on how to achieve this.

1.3 Woodland terms and concepts

The most important and widely used terms and concepts in forest and woodland management are described here and in the glossary (Appendix II). These and other useful terms are highlighted in bold the first time they appear in the text and are also explained in the glossary. Some terms have different meanings to foresters and to conservationists, or the same feature may be described in different ways, and you will need to understand these distinctions in order to follow properly any advice you are given.

Woodland refers to any area of land that is mainly covered by trees, although it does not include orchards and parkland. **Forest** has a similar meaning but is usually applied to larger areas of land, particularly **coniferous plantations**. (Sometimes the term 'forest' has a different meaning, when it is applied to areas set aside for large game, such as the New Forest or deer forests, which in places may be devoid of trees. The word will not be used in this sense here.)

Both **forestry** and **silviculture** refer to the cultivation of trees as a crop to produce timber, and are the woodland equivalents of farming and agriculture. **Afforestation** is the planting of trees on land that has been unwooded in the recent past.

Tree structure and development

A new tree can originate from a seed, a **cutting** or a **layer** from the shoots or a **sucker** from the roots of an older tree. As shown in Figure 1.2, the seedling or very young tree usually has one main stem, known as the **trunk** or **bole** in older trees, which carries the **leader** or main top shoot of the tree. Side shoots or branches from the main stem carry the leaves of the tree, and these spreading branches and foliage make up its **crown**.

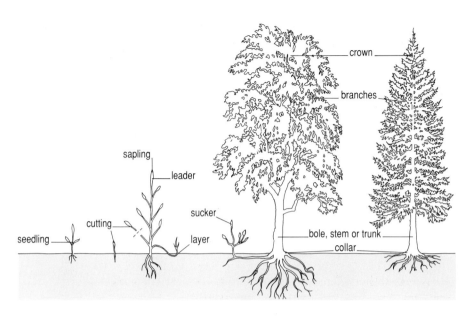

Figure 1.2   Tree structure

Woodland structure

In many areas of woodland you will find trees of different sizes and ages and also other types of plants forming several layers in the vertical **structure**, from the woodland floor to the tree **canopy** (see Figure 1.3).

Often, three layers of vegetation can be seen beneath the tree canopy – **shrub, field** and **ground layers** – consisting of woody shrubs, herbaceous plants and mosses respectively. The trees of the canopy and shrub layers may include

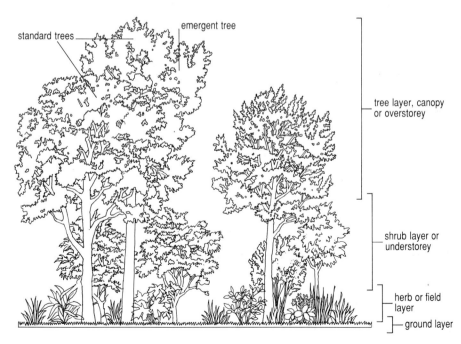

Figure 1.3   Woodland structure

9

individuals of the same species but of different ages and sizes, or different species which reach varying heights when mature. For example, in oak woodland, if enough light reaches the ground layer, there will be some young oaks that will eventually grow to replace the trees presently forming the canopy, and other species like elder which will never grow tall enough to reach the canopy. The field and ground layers will also contain the seedlings or suckers of the plants in the taller layers.

Woodlands have horizontal as well as vertical structure. For example, the density of the canopy can vary – if the crowns of the trees meet and do not allow sunlight to reach the layers directly below, the canopy is described as closed (except in winter in **deciduous** woodland); if there are gaps in the canopy that allow sunlight to reach the lower layers even in summer, it is described as open. An open canopy occurs when natural features like ponds, rivers or steep rocky ground prevent trees from growing, where artificial clearings (such as **rides** or **glades**) have been created to allow access or to encourage game, or where areas have been felled or damaged by a gale or grazing animals.

Diversity in the woodland structure, both horizontal and vertical, is usually beneficial to wildlife and landscape conservation.

Woodland development

The structure of a **stand** of trees or a complete woodland varies according to its stage of development, and whether it has arisen by **natural regeneration** or through active planting (see Figure 1.4). If the wood is planted, seedlings or saplings are usually grown in a nursery and planted on the site (plantations), rather than tree seeds being sown directly on site. Once established, the trees (with some thinning) are allowed to grow to maturity and become **standards**, usually as **high forest**, or are regularly cut nearer the ground to encourage new growth from the resulting stumps (or **stools**) as **coppice** wood.

Woodland established by natural regeneration is likely to have an uneven-aged open canopy while plantation woodland is more likely to have an even-aged, closed canopy.

As already mentioned, there are subtle differences in the meaning of some terms used by conservationists and silviculturalists; the main ones are summarised in Table 1.1. These differences arise because silviculturalists are interested mainly in the trees or timber crop within the woodland, while conservationists consider the whole community, the fungi, birds, insects, mosses, herbs, woody shrubs and so on, as well as the trees that help to form the woodland ecosystem.

1.4 How to use this book

Readers of this book may be involved in managing many different types of woodland, from extensive plantations of coniferous forest to small **copses** in the corners of arable fields. Your motivation could be a simple delight in the variety of wildlife that can be attracted to carefully planned and well managed woodland or it could be a need to make as much money as possible from it, or any combination of the two. You may want to encourage game or create an attractive area for public recreation. Woodland can fulfill a wide variety of needs.

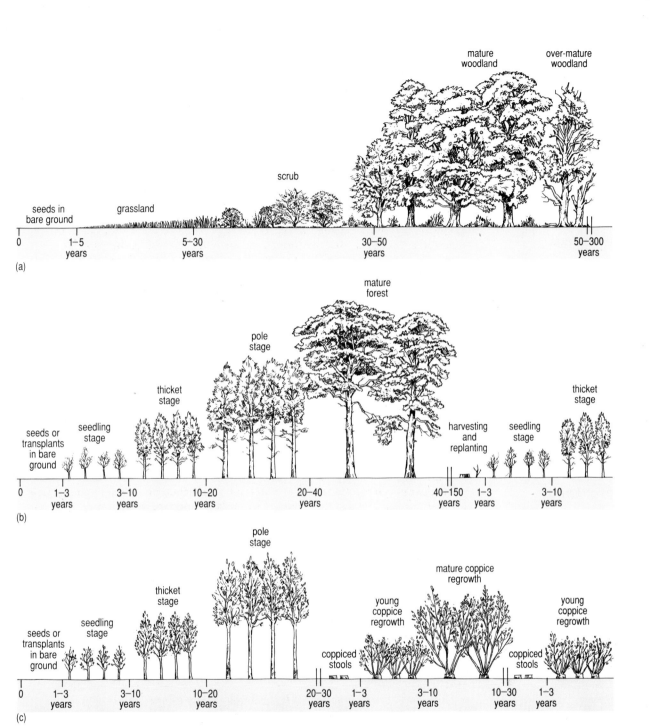

(a)

seeds in bare ground | grassland | scrub | mature woodland | over-mature woodland

0 | 1–5 years | 5–30 years | 30–50 years | 50–300 years

(b)

seeds or transplants in bare ground | seedling stage | thicket stage | pole stage | mature forest | harvesting and replanting | seedling stage | thicket stage

0 | 1–3 years | 3–10 years | 10–20 years | 20–40 years | 40–150 years | 1–3 years | 3–10 years

(c)

seeds or transplants in bare ground | seedling stage | thicket stage | pole stage | coppiced stools | young coppice regrowth | mature coppice regrowth | coppiced stools | young coppice regrowth

0 | 1–3 years | 3–10 years | 10–20 years | 20–30 years | 1–3 years | 3–10 years | 10–30 years | 1–3 years

General information on sources of advice and grants is given in the two supplementary booklets of the foundation module, *Helpful Organisations* and *Legislation and Regulations*, and will not be repeated here. There has also not been space to go into detail about commercial timber production, but this subject is covered by several of the books listed in Appendix I. Both this book and the accompanying video cassette refer to the practical skills needed and safety aspects of woodland management, but there is no substitute for

Figure 1.4   Types of woodland cycles or rotational systems:
(a) natural regeneration;
(b) planted high forest;
(c) coppice

11

Table 1.1 Terms applied to woodland development and their meanings (see also Figure 1.4)

Term	Conservation meaning	Silviculture meaning
Scrub	Successional stage (or climax community) where the main woody species are shrubs rather than trees, and any trees present are small	Crops where most of the trees are small, of poor form and/or timber potential and/or are unmarketable species
Thicket stage	–	Stage after planting when the young trees have grown up to form a dense thicket or clump
Pole stage	–	Stage when the young trees resemble tall, thin poles between thicket and maturity
Dominant species	The most abundant species (usually trees) present in an area; less often, the species which most influences the character of the woodland community	Trees with most of their crown within the main canopy. They may not be the most abundant species overall
Mature trees	Large trees, forming part of the main forest canopy, with no obvious signs of dying such as large dead branches and rotting trunks	Trees which have reached the stage of growth where it is financially optimal to harvest them (i.e. where the mean annual increment in volume or financial terms reaches a maximum). Usually younger than mature trees in conservation terms
High forest	–	Stands where at least half the trees are marketable as timber
Over-mature trees	Large trees which are beginning to die, with many dead branches and well-advanced decay in the trunks	Trees which have passed the point of maturity defined above. They may still be growing well and be sound in trunk and branch

experience and you should, if necessary, attend a training course that will show you how to handle tools and machines correctly.

The video cassette complements this book. Many aspects of woodland conservation and management have an important visual element and are best conveyed by colour pictures. For example, wildlife assessment needs the ability to recognise the key species in an area, particularly trees and other plants. Landscape assessment takes a broader look at the area as a whole and the place of woodland within it. Many of the activities involved in managing woodland, from planting trees to coppicing, are best demonstrated by a moving picture. In Box 1.1 the contents of the video cassette and how they relate to this book are outlined. Throughout this book the marginal flag ▣ indicates topics that are dealt with further in the video cassette.

12

Box 1.1   The video cassette: A video guide to woodland management

The 30 minute video cassette which accompanies this book is a blend of moving and still pictures, interviews and demonstrations to illustrate further and inform you of practical conservation measures in all types of woodland. It has been designed so that it can be watched either in a single viewing or section by section. As with this book, the emphasis is on assessment, options and implementation. Links between the book and the video cassette are marked by marginal flags▭.

The video cassette consists of the following.

Band 1   *If you go down in the woods today* – Types, origins, structure and purpose of woodland in Great Britain. How to assess your woodland.

Band 2   *Woods in the landscape* – Assessment and design of both broad-leaved and coniferous woodland.

Band 3   *Traditional methods of woodland management* – The art of coppicing and other techniques and safety in the wood.

Band 4   *Paying for conservation* – Ways of getting something back from woodland management.

Band 5   *The dark forest – shed a little light* – Methods of integrating commercial forestry and wildlife.

Band 6   *Great oaks from little acorns grow* – Creating new woods and monitoring their success.

Band 7   *A woodland management checklist* – A summary of what to do to conserve wildlife and landscape.

If you work through this book from beginning to end, you will have a good understanding of woodland management in all its contexts. However, you may want to be more selective, to concentrate at one particular time on assessment or on implementation, or to cover only one particular type of woodland such as small broad-leaved woods on farms. To enable you to do this easily, Chapters 2, 3 and 4 deal with integrated assessment, Chapters 5 and 6 with management options for established and new woodland respectively and Chapter 7 with implementation and the techniques used to fulfil the options. The examples used in this book illustrate the activities described and show you how to do them yourself. They are drawn chiefly from two case studies, one dealing with large scale, mainly coniferous forest in an upland area, and the other with small areas of woodland on a lowland farm. They are mainly in special case study sections at the end of each chapter and collectively give a complete picture of woodland planning for practical conservation.

Each chapter also has an exercise for you to do, printed on a green background. These are based on what you have read and should be done on an area of woodland to which you have legitimate access. The case study sections which follow these exercises will give you a wide enough range of examples to cover most of the situations you might choose.

This book provides enough information for you to take full account of the needs of conservation when managing woodland. But it is important to stress that, if you are not already a qualified woodland or forest manager, it won't turn you into one. Under these circumstances you should take expert advice and, if necessary, hire contractors to do the work involved in any woodland management you are planning.

1.5   The case studies

The following descriptions form the background to the two case studies.

Atholl Estate woodlands

The Atholl Estate near Dunkeld in Highland Perthshire has some 300 years of recorded woodland management, for timber production, for shelter for game and wildlife and for its beauty and landscape value. In 1686 a variety of broad-leaved and coniferous trees was planted for aesthetic reasons, while around 1700 oak was fairly extensively planted on a 21-year coppice **rotation** for tanning, and ash was a much-favoured tree for clumps and hedges. More recently hybrid larch, which originated on this estate, was planted and sheep were grazed beneath the light deciduous crown of these trees and of European larch.

A feature of the estate, in common with other large estates in the area, has been large-scale **clear felling** in this 'big' landscape, especially to support the war effort in the First and Second World Wars.

A woodland **Dedication Scheme** was introduced on the estate in 1946, when the national demand was 'to create a reserve of timber to be used in time of emergency'. This had generally encouraged the cutting of mature broad-leaved and mixed stands in order to replace them with faster-growing coniferous species. The tax system of the time also encouraged the large-scale felling of timber without replanting, adding to the large amount of bare woodland ground resulting from major past **windblows**. When the present manager took over in 1977 there were approximately 480 hectares of cut or windblown woodlands requiring replanting under the terms of the Dedication Scheme.

Action taken

The action agreed with the current manager in 1977 was:

▶   to survey the woods to measure the growing timber stock and increment, and from this to decide on a realistic cutting programme that would provide a long-term, sustainable yield of timber;

▶   to stop clear felling for a minimum period of 5 years;

▶   to replant felled and windblown areas, accepting natural regeneration where suitable;

▶   to reduce staff by natural wastage to take unrealistic pressure off woodland finances and to set up some of the existing staff as contractors;

▶   to restrict the under-grazing of larch and zone it to encourage both natural regeneration of trees and the growth of natural plants and associated fauna;

▶   to review the species used for replanting.

Owner's attitude

The owner's attitude is one of complete support for a well-balanced policy aimed at low input forestry with restricted cutting to allow the structure of the forest to return to a more natural condition. This is integrated with a high sporting interest, and recreational use by the general public, together with a keen awareness of the landscape value of this highly sensitive area, where tourism is an important source of income.

The production of timber is essential to maintain the ongoing forest programme and to finance vital maintenance, and it is the prime objective for the bulk of the forest. However, it is always considered together with game, shelter, amenity and other conservation aspects, such as the presence of several **Sites of Special Scientific Interest** (SSSIs) within the woodland.

The cost penalty of these policies is accepted by the owner, and such constraints are not seen as a serious problem. The various interests rarely result in an 'either/or' situation but generally an integration, with certain areas given a positive priority for game, amenity or conservation considerations, without ever losing sight of the crop. The key is discussion, decision and timing – DDT!

A large estate like this is always broken down into smaller areas for management purposes. This case study will concentrate on Killiehangie Hill. This is an area of mainly coniferous forest, at the **pole** or **thinning** stage. Just as it is reaching the stage where it will begin to provide an income, the area is suffering from severe deer damage to the bark of the trees. This will cause a weakness in the trunk which will reduce the commercial value of the timber and may also cause the trunk to snap at that point during gales. The estate boundary at the top of the hill has been marked by an old dry stone wall which is slowly collapsing. The area has never been deer-proof, but the animals have not caused any serious problems until recently. The damage is mainly caused by over-wintering stags that may have been forced into the woods because of afforestation and deer-fencing on other areas of their open-hill habitat. The need to take some action over this problem is the main reason for re-assessing the area in detail at this time.

Small woods in Sussex

The second case study is based on a lowland farm, which lies within the South Downs Area of Outstanding Natural Beauty and also partly within the South Downs Environmentally Sensitive Area.

The farm occupies 408 hectares on six different soil types. Approximately 230 hectares are owner-occupied, the remainder being rented. Woodland and **scrub** occupy 11% of the farm area and the rest is a mixture of arable crops, temporary and permanent improved grassland and rough grazing.

The farm was chosen because it offers a wide range of landscape and habitat features and includes several mature woodland blocks, probably requiring a range of different management regimes. The farm manager is fully occupied with making a worthwhile return on the business but is willing to accommodate conservation in his planning and decision-making.

Treatment of the case studies

The case studies deal with very different situations and were done by different people. They therefore do not parallel one another exactly – each stresses different aspects and adopts a slightly different approach to woodland management. This emphasises the fact that there are no right and wrong ways to manage land – only more or less effective ways, and what is most effective will vary according to circumstances.

Chapter 2

WOODLAND LANDSCAPE ASSESSMENT

Woodland has a considerable impact on the landscape. Trees are tall so woods are highly visible. They cloak the land, sometimes softening rugged features, and providing shapes and colours that contrast with other features of the landscape such as fields and rivers, hedgerows and walls. Many people also enjoy walking through woodland to experience its sights, smells and sounds, its size and apparent timelessness and historical associations.

As Box 2.1 shows, woodland managers, like most people with an interest in conservation, have an intense appreciation of their surroundings, including the impact of woodlands on the landscape. They are also in a position to influence the landscape when planning changes to woodland or thinking of planting a new wood, and the starting point for any major woodland activity should be a landscape assessment.

2.1   General landscape assessment

Landscape assessment in general involves gaining an overall impression of the land and of how the details fit together to make up the whole picture. This will depend on the variation, from one area to another, in:

▶ the landform (the underlying skeleton of rocks and soil);

▶ the covering of vegetation;

▶ the buildings and historical and archaeological features (structures);

▶ the cultural associations of the area concerned;

▶ the human needs it fulfils.

The assessment should also reflect people's attitudes and social influences. Landscape is a valuable public resource and should be assessed and planned with this in mind.

General landscape assessment was described in the foundation book. It involves: selecting several viewpoints to give a complete coverage of the area you are interested in; marking these on a map of the area and filling in a checklist for each viewpoint; and recording your impressions formally using notes, photographs, sketches and maps (not forgetting to consider your personal preferences and perceptions and the needs and desires of other people who may have an interest in the area). It is important to keep systematic records and, if appropriate, to divide the holding up into clearly recognisable zones to provide a basis for the long-term management of the land.

For a more detailed assessment, concentrating on the areas of existing woodland, focus your attention particularly on:

▶ the shape of the woodland;

▶ the scale of the woodland;

▶ the diversity of the woodland in structure and species composition;

▶ the ability of the woodland to screen an eyesore or a hide a beautiful view;

Box 2.1   A forester's view

Yesterday I was marking for thinning a 60 acre plantation of oak in its middle years – past the leggy 'adolescent' stage and showing signs of promise, despite growing on a site more suited to larches and pines and the fact that its life had started on a coppice rotation for the tanning industry. There were **maiden** stems throughout the crop, some of these with a distinctly Spessart appearance about them. At the base of a flourishing coppice stool were two stems about 3 or 4 inches in diameter, some 4 feet high and about 3 feet apart, long since dead but seasoned a hard iron-grey. Despite the passing years the moss-covered tops retained a groove cut down into the top of each stem.

I was at the edge of this high wood with views across the magnificent Perthshire countryside noisy with the clamouring of geese on the loch below and enriched by the late afternoon sun glinting on the mixed Sitka spruce and larch plantation on the opposite bank – a warm snug wood into which the feeding wild pheasants on the lower stubble would shortly go to roost since this particular oak wood with its clean forest floor was too cold and inhospitable for much wildlife at this time of the year.

My thoughts went back 30 years or more to Sussex oak woods and coppice, and sharpening the old-fashioned saw secured in two stems, similar to those I had just spotted. It was a busy thriving forest world with long traditions. I recalled the Juniper brothers and father cleaving coppice oak into arris rails and morticed posts with chestnut, hazel and ash being fashioned into spekewood, sheep hurdles, thatching spars, Sussex trug baskets, fencing stakes and umpteen other items. This wood too must have been a flourishing place with the oak being cut and stripped of its bark for tanning, and the local larch going down to Friarton Harbour in Perth for export in the early nineteenth century, a long time before export pulp to Scandinavia!

This time last year with an abundance of acorns the wood was blue with pigeons; this year there are none and the grey squirrels which rose in numbers in response to food will decline again. Despite all this, some seedling oak survived and this thinning will provide **brash** to protect some of them, the light will enable a little vegetation to flourish (I must remember to high prune some selected stems after next summer) and the crowns of some of the remaining trees will respond. The life of the wood has been extended and enriched by thinning – all made possible by a small immediate financial return on the timber.

Chris Langton, Atholl Estate, Perthshire

> the presence of any features of archaeological interest;
> footpaths and public viewpoints of the woodland.

If you are planning to plant new woodland, you first need to consider whether this is the best use of the site, involving if possible the development of a general management plan, as outlined in Chapter 1.

In assessing the landscape in this way, personal preferences and fashion are involved to some extent. However, there are a few widely accepted rules to guide you, at least until you have the self-confidence and experience to develop your own methods. Note how, in each case below, it is particularly important to consider the areas of woodland in relation to the surrounding landscape.

Shape of the woodland

The accepted orthodoxy is that long straight edges, sharp angles, parallel edges, symmetrical shapes, narrow strips and (on hillsides) vertical and horizontal boundaries all detract from the apparent 'naturalness' of the

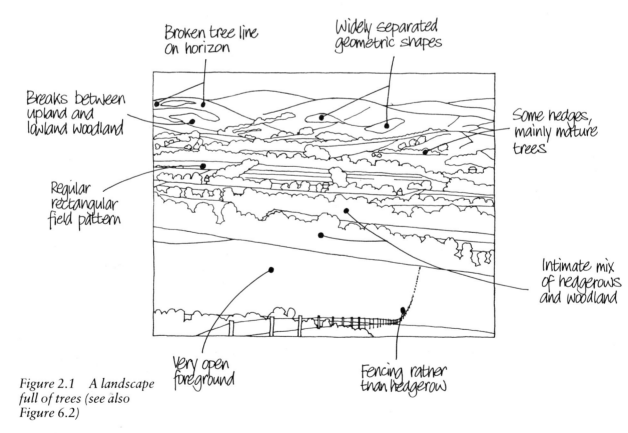

Broken tree line on horizon

Widely separated geometric shapes

Breaks between upland and lowland woodland

Some hedges, mainly mature trees

Regular rectangular field pattern

Intimate mix of hedgerows and woodland

Very open foreground

Fencing rather than hedgerow

Figure 2.1   A landscape full of trees (see also Figure 6.2)

landscape and so are undesirable. Conversely, areas of woodland that have irregular shapes and follow natural features such as escarpments, river banks, valleys or rounded hills are desirable landscape features.

However, there are no hard or fast rules about this. In farmed areas, particularly where there are many small fields and hedges, small strips of woodland or larger rectangular blocks that are in keeping with the shapes of the surrounding fields are perfectly acceptable. Note how, in Figure 2.1, the straight shelterbelt boundaries are quite in keeping with the character of the valley landscape, but look intrusive when extended too far up the hillside.

Woodland has a particularly noticeable effect on the landscape at the skyline. In flatter areas, a covering of trees on a low hill can increase its apparent height and give it a greater impact. On the other hand, a clear break in a line of trees on the skyline looks unnatural.

Scale of the woodland

Generally speaking, a larger scale landscape is one with wide areas of land visible for a considerable distance. In smaller scale landscapes the views are shorter and more restricted, and distinctive features are closer together. In Figure 2.1 in the large scale hilly landscape in the background, small blocks of trees, widely separated from one another, look intrusive and unnatural. On the other hand, in the lowland area in the figure, it is the size of the spaces between the wooded areas that determines the scale, giving a much more intimate appearance to the foreground, despite the wide area of land visible. In intensively farmed areas where most of the hedges and trees have been removed, even lowland landscapes will be large scale and there is a danger that the small remaining areas of woodland will appear fussy and detached from the landscape as a whole. However, small clumps of trees in an otherwise treeless landscape are likely to become locally known and loved landmarks, for example Chanctonbury Ring on the Sussex Downs or Brailles Hill in Warwickshire. A small group of trees planted in a hollow or narrow valley will have very little landscape impact.

Diversity of the woodland

Landscape diversity in woodland arises partly from the presence of a range of tree species which will give a varied pattern of shapes and colours throughout the year. As a general rule, two or three main species of tree, with a few others scattered about, will give the necessary diversity without being fussy. However, if the different species have been planted in a regular pattern it will detract from the overall effect. In addition, a varied age structure and a partially open canopy encourage a more varied understorey in the wood. Where attempts have been made to increase diversity at the woodland edge, particularly in coniferous woodland, an irregularly shaped band will look better than a regular one.

Views and screens

When walking within a wood, glades and clearings that allow an occasional longer view are often especially attractive features. The internal landscape of a wood can be boring and depressing, particularly where trees are closely planted or where you walk for miles without any breaks in the trees. In some areas, trees can hide a beautiful view, in winter as well as in summer if they are

You see - it's now had a Tree Preservation Order placed on it...

evergreen conifers, so it is important to think about what the woods are screening as well as about the landscape value of the woods themselves.

The screening ability of trees can, of course, be put to good advantage in concealing ugly landscape features such as unsightly buildings, dumps or machinery yards. So, when doing your landscape assessment, think about whether any of the woodland has this function and also about whether there are eyesores that could be screened in this way. Similarly, views within a woodland can vary with the seasons, and woodland operations such as felling will open up previously hidden features.

Archaeological features

Trees are the oldest living things in the countryside, and **ancient woodland** in particular can contain a wealth of archaeological sites. Ancient barrows, camps, mounds, hollows and boundary earthworks are valuable as features of the landscape in their own right, as places of interest for visitors and as sites for rare plants and animals, as well as being 'time capsules' of information about the past.

Trees, however, can damage ancient monuments through the action of their roots and hide them from public view. It is therefore important to recognise and note down the features of any such sites to help plan their conservation. Some sites are easily visible but others may be buried and require detective work using old maps or observations of changes in vegetation to reveal their presence.

Conserving ancient monuments which have survived for many years need not be at odds with current land practices. Indeed, grants may be available for their repair and upkeep. Advice and help on all these matters is available from your local county archaeological officer and other national bodies listed in the *Helpful Organisations* booklet from the foundation module.

The public interest

The person who owns or manages a piece of land inevitably sees it differently from outsiders. Any landscape assessment should take account of both points of view – those of the manager of the land or the person who has the power to

20

take decisions about it, and those of members of the public who may drive past it, walk through it or view it from a distance. Where there are footpaths or other public access to woodland you should watch out for any dead or dying trees that might be dangerous, but avoid clearing all dead wood for the sake of tidiness alone. Dead trees can be just as interesting to look at as living ones, so long as there are not too many of them, and they are an important wildlife habitat in their own right.

In some particularly important landscape areas a public interest has been formally declared by their designation as National Parks, Areas of Outstanding Natural Beauty (AONBs) in England and Wales or National Scenic Areas (NSAs) in Scotland and individual trees or small woods may be protected by Tree Preservation Orders (TPOs), where trees cannot be felled or branches cut without permission from the planning authority. You always need to be aware of any special restrictions on the management of your woodland (see the *Legislation and Regulations* booklet of the foundation module).

2.2 *Making your own woodland landscape assessment*

In the previous section the features of landscape assessment are described, but the only way to learn more is to do it for yourself.

As suggested in Chapter 1, choose an area of woodland to which you have legitimate access and make a landscape assessment of it. Remember that, ideally, you should first assess the place of the woodland in the landscape as a whole, as described in the foundation book and summarised briefly here, before going on to assess the woodland areas themselves. At this stage you should use maps to mark viewpoints and significant features, and photographs, sketches and checklists to record the *present* state of the landscape as a basis for planning changes and as a reference point against which to measure the effects of these changes. Some of these methods are developed further in Chapter 6 where various future plans and landscape design options are explored and evaluated for their impact in relation to the wildlife and business assessments.

General landscape assessment

1   Draw a sketch map of your area (or use an Ordnance survey map) and mark prominent features within, and outside, it. Annotate the map with comments on these features and mark any distinct landscape zones.

2   Make sketches or take photographs showing distant views of the woodland. Mark each viewpoint on your map. Include any viewpoints that are important to the general public, for example views of the woods from main roads or villages, as well as those of personal interest to the land owner or manager. Attach for each photograph or sketch a note describing:

▶   the viewpoint from which it was taken;

▶   the reason for choosing that viewpoint, particularly noting anything of public interest;

▶   the shape of the woodland areas;

▶   the scale of the woodland areas;

▶   your personal perceptions.

(Note that these guidelines are for existing woodland. Where new woodlands are being considered the assessment should be based on a full general management planning exercise, as summarised in Section 1.1.)

1   Draw a sketch map of the woodland itself, dividing it into **compartments** if necessary and marking any distinctive landscape features. Make close-up sketches or take photographs of the woodland areas, including views from outside and from inside the woods, particularly of notable features such as glades or ponds. Identify any areas with particularly interesting characteristics such as old boundary ditches and/or ridges. As in (2) above, for each sketch mark the viewpoint on your map and add notes describing:

▶   the viewpoint from which it was taken;

▶   the reason for choosing the viewpoint, particularly noting anything of public interest;

▶   the diversity of the woodland;

▶   historical and archaeological features;

▶   the screening effect of the woodland on eyesores and/or beautiful views;

▶   your personal perceptions.

2   Record any restrictions relevant to the role of the woodland in the landscape or to the treatment of individual trees:

▶   National Parks (in England and Wales);

▶   AONBs (in England and Wales);

▶   NSAs (in Scotland);

▶   Conservation Areas;

▶   TPOs;

▶   public access, footpaths, bridleways;

▶   ancient monuments.

2.3   Landscape assessment of case study areas

The following examples of woodland landscape assessment, based on the two case studies described at the end of Chapter 1, will give you some guidance but remember they are personal views. Do not treat them as rigid templates – as you become more experienced you will develop your own variations on the method, and the area you are concerned with may have different features from the examples used here.

Killiehangie Hill, Atholl Estate

Geologically, the area is a rocky outcrop with a sandy soil derived from mica schist. Drainage is poor in some areas, resulting in shallow bog conditions. The height ranges from 80 metres at the riverside to over 300 metres at the tops of the hills. The vegetation cover is mainly woodland but there is some arable land to the west of the river on the lower slopes of the hill. The aspect is mainly north-east, but the 'toe' of the hill has a chiefly north to south-east aspect with a distinct dividing ridge. Distant views are spacious, with a mountainous skyline.

The two viewpoints selected for detailed landscape assessment are shown in Figure 2.2 which is a map of Killiehangie Hill and the surrounding area,

Figure 2.2   Landscape assessment map of Killiehangie Hill

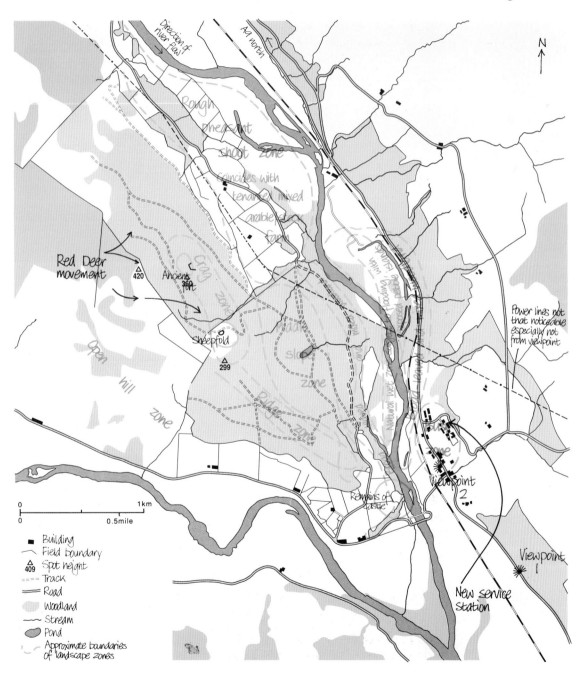

Map annotations:
- Direction of river flow
- A9 North
- N
- Rough pheasant shoot zone coincides with tenanted mixed arable farm
- Red Deer movement
- Crag zone
- △ 420
- Ancients 360m
- Sheepfold
- △ 299
- open hill zone
- main slope zone
- Ridge zone
- Natural wet zone
- Island along here especially
- Power lines not that noticeable especially not from viewpoint
- Remains of castle
- Viewpoint 2
- Viewpoint 1
- New service station

Legend:
- 0 — 1km
- 0 — 0.5mile
- ■ Building
- ⌒ Field boundary
- △ 409 Spot height
- ==== Track
- === Road
- Woodland
- ⌒ Stream
- ⬭ Pond
- Approximate boundaries of landscape zones

23

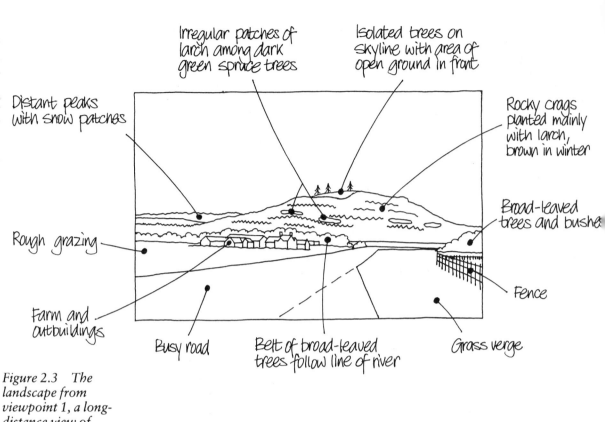

Irregular patches of larch among dark green spruce trees

Isolated trees on skyline with area of open ground in front

Distant peaks with snow patches

Rocky crags planted mainly with larch, brown in winter

Broad-leaved trees and bushes

Rough grazing

Fence

Farm and outbuildings

Busy road

Belt of broad-leaved trees follow line of river

Grass verge

Figure 2.3 The landscape from viewpoint 1, a long-distance view of Killiehangie Hill, as seen by tourists travelling north on the A9

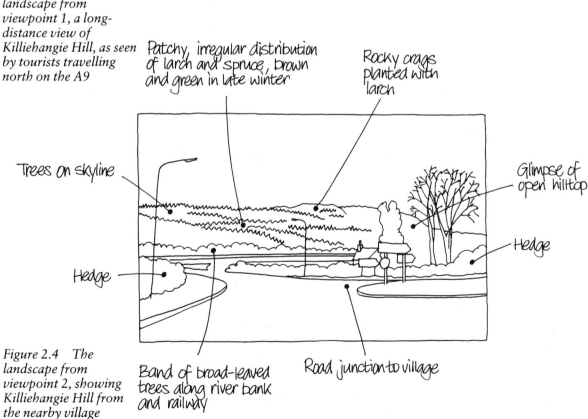

Patchy, irregular distribution of larch and spruce, brown and green in late winter

Rocky crags planted with larch

Trees on skyline

Glimpse of open hilltop

Hedge

Hedge

Band of broad-leaved trees along river bank and railway

Road junction to village

Figure 2.4 The landscape from viewpoint 2, showing Killiehangie Hill from the nearby village

including landscape zones and the location of historical features. Figures 2.3 and 2.4 show the landscape from viewpoints 1 and 2.

Viewpoint 1

From here, there is a fairly long-distance view of Killiehangie Hill with its pleasing mixture of chiefly coniferous trees, but the area is highly visible from cars travelling north on the A9. The hill is a rising landform between the rivers Tummel and Tay. There is a traditional stone farm building in front of the viewpoint with mixed woodland to the east nearby, where the old route of the A9 can be seen fenced off. The farmland is a narrow fertile arable strip down to the River Tay to the west, with snow-capped mountains beyond.

The hill is not as flat as it appears from here, and the middle ground, looking along the valley, is undulating. The rolling effect of ridges and knolls helps to reduce the impact of straight features such as roads and walls.

Viewpoint 2

Killiehangie Hill rises fairly steeply across the river valley from here with undulating slopes on to ridges and some very steep crags and cliffs. The commercial species are mainly Norway and Sitka spruce which provide a deep green background, broken up by deciduous larch and broad-leaved trees such as birch, which are particularly beautiful in spring and autumn. The presence of some old dry stone walls and a sheep-fold within the forested area indicate that this land has been farmed in the past, and a ruined hill fort (a scheduled ancient monument) is evidence of more ancient habitation although it is not really a feature – perhaps it should be.

In the middle distance, the river and railway are not very noticeable as they are screened by trees – oak, birch, willow and some Scots pine, gradually giving way to coniferous woodland on the hill. In such a scenic area, this is an excellent example of sympathetic coniferous planting, with native broad-leaves in the middle and foreground.

The hillside is more openly visible from here than from the first viewpoint and it is seen by slower traffic travelling on the minor roads and also by people in the local pub and nearby café. The pub is a traditional building while the café is part of a new and very busy service station used largely by heavy lorries. Immediately in front of these buildings, close to the viewpoint, are some attractive old stone buildings and a working smithy. To the west of the A9 is the village playing field. Ballinluig Cross (a very large monument) is slowly disappearing behind growing trees. Nearby, there are the remains of an old castle. Ballinluig is an attractive, practical, working village with strong farming, forestry and game connections.

The landscape features from this viewpoint are summarised in Table 2.1, using the checklist in Section 2.3 of the foundation book.

General landscape assessment

The landscape assessment criteria described in Section 2.2 have mainly been covered in the above summary but some additional points about the public interest remain to be made.

The area has a long tradition of management as forest, so local people are well-used to change as the forest goes through the various stages of the management cycle from replanting to cutting. These operations are most obvious from a high viewpoint, across the main valley, a view seen chiefly by farmers and others working on the land, who understand the processes involved.

However, this is also a major tourist area and, as indicated above, diversity in the shapes of compartments and in species composition have been encouraged,

Table 2.1 Checklist of landscape features: landform, vegetation and structure

Grade the relative contribution of each feature as follows: ∗inconspicuous; ∗∗noticeable; ∗∗∗conspicuous

Land holding *Killinagie Hill, Atholl Estate* Viewpoint no. *2 Ballinluig Inn at road junction with A9.*

Date *4/5/89* Time of day *Late afternoon*

Weather *Sunny, windy.*

Landform

Plain	Coast	Marsh	Lake
Lowland	Estuary	Mudflat	Pond
Plateau	Broad valley ∗∗∗	Dune	River ∗
Hill ∗∗∗	Narrow valley	Beach	Stream
Crag or cliff ∗∗∗	Deep gorge		Canal
Mountain			Ditch

Slopes

Vertical (Steep) (Gently sloping)
(Undulating) Flat

Vegetation

Woodland
Broad-leaved woodland
Coniferous woodland ∗∗∗
Mixed woodland ∗∗
Scrub

Heathland and grassland
Heather moorland ∗ *in distance*
Upland grass moor
Peat bog
Water meadow
Bracken
Lowland heath
Lowland unimproved grassland

Cultivated land
Arable land
Improved pasture
Market gardens and orchards
Parkland

Linear features
Hedgerows
Woodland fringe ∗∗∗
River banks ∗
Roadside verges ∗
Railway embankments ∗

River, railway and road run through the area in north–south direction but are largely screened by trees.

Small isolated features
Isolated trees
Groups of trees, mainly
broad-leaved (less than 0.25 ha)
Groups of trees, mainly coniferous
(less than 0.25 ha)
Small shelter-belts
Copses and spinneys
Small gardens

Structures

Buildings ∗∗∗
Farmyards ∗
Camp sites
Car parks ∗∗∗
Quarries
Industrial land

Fences
Walls ∗∗ — *Boundary wall marking vegetation change from heather/grass pasture to woodland to the*
Telephone wires
Electricity pylons ∗ *north-west (this is where red deer are entering the forest from neighbouring hills)*
Rubbish dumps
Derelict land

partly with this in mind and also because it suits the natural inclinations of the manager. There is public access on foot to the forest on Killiehangie Hill, but not many people take advantage of it.

The landscape perception aspects of the area, showing how it appears to the forest manager, are summarised in Table 2.2, as suggested in Section 2.3 of the foundation book.

Table 2.2 Landscape perception of Killiehangie Hill

Criterion	Description
Scale	Large (over 200 hectares of woodland in a wide, spacious landscape)
Enclosure	Generally open to exposed
Variety/diversity	Varied and pleasing
Harmony	Well-balanced
Movement	A9 and service area frantic; woods generally peaceful (busy every fifth year due to thinning operations)
Texture	Smooth in summer, harsh in winter
Naturalness	Wild and unmanaged on the forest fringes; relatively un-natural elsewhere
Tidiness	Relatively untidy
Colour	Subtle
Smell	Pleasant, particularly within the forest
Sound	Quiet in woods, noisy at viewpoints
Rarity	Common in the locality
Security	Varies from comfortable to downright dangerous
Stimulus	Varied, invigorating and peaceful in parts
Beauty	Attractive, beautiful, rugged (from viewpoints); from within, varied from ordinary to quite striking (especially views out from the woodland).

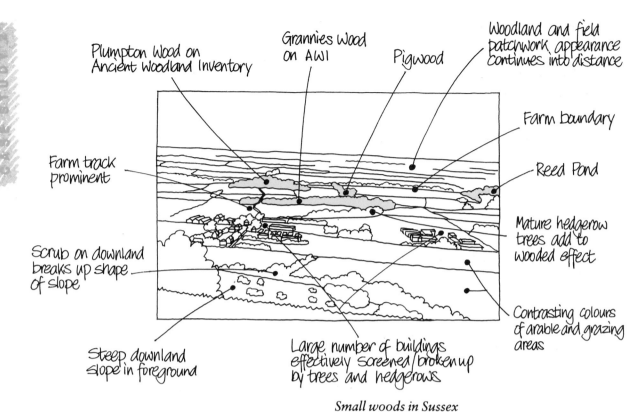

Plumpton Wood on Ancient Woodland Inventory

Grannies Wood on AWI

Pigwood

Woodland and field patchwork appearance continues into distance

Farm boundary

Reed Pond

Farm track prominent

Mature hedgerow trees add to wooded effect

Scrub on downland breaks up shape of slope

Steep downland slope in foreground

Large number of buildings effectively screened/broken up by trees and hedgerows

Contrasting colours of arable and grazing areas

Small woods in Sussex

Figure 2.5 Annotated sketch of the case study farm from a viewpoint on the ridge of the chalk escarpment

(Please note that this is not comprehensive and concentrates on the major features.)

The case study farm lies on both sides of a road at the foot of the north escarpment of the South Downs. To the north of the main buildings lies gently undulating ground falling to the northern boundary, and consisting of soils based mainly on Gault Clay, Lower Greensand and Alluvial Drift. To the south of the road there are five fields at the foot of the escarpment which rises sharply to the ridge path known as the South Downs Way. In clear weather this vantage point has excellent views northward across the Weald (see Figure 2.5 and Table 2.3) and southwards to the English Channel. This escarpment and the gently sloping plateau lie on chalk deposits.

General landscape assessment

The landform falls into three distinct zones (lowland plain, very steep downland slope and upland plain; see Figure 2.6) which also greatly influence land use (see Section 4.4). Several archaeological and historical features are also present, the most visible being on the Downs. Woodland and scrub occupy 11% of the farm area and are most obvious from the rights of way on the escarpment, although much is visible from the main road. There are eight main woodland blocks ranging in size from 0.5 to 7.1 hectares, six of them lying on the heavy Gault Clays on the lower part of the farm. All the woods are broad-leaved and the four largest are included in the Nature Conservancy Council's (NCC) Ancient Woodland Inventory (AWI). The latter have a coppice-with-standards structure but have been irregularly managed since the 1940s. Some damage was done by the great storm of 1987.

Woodland landscape assessment

Consideration of three of the eight woodland blocks will illustrate the different management needs.

Table 2.3 Checklist of landscape features: landform, vegetation and structure

Grade the relative contribution of each feature as follows: ★inconspicuous; ★★noticeable; ★★★conspicuous

Land holding ......~~Sussex Case Study Farm~~ Viewpoint no. 1...............................

Date   ......May 1989................ Time of day   Morning......................

Weather   ......Warm, sunny and hazy...

Landform

Plain ★★★	Coast	Marsh	Lake
Lowland	Estuary	Mudflat	Pond ★
Plateau ★★	Broad valley	Dune	River
Hill ★★★	Narrow valley	Beach	Stream ★
Crag or cliff	Deep gorge		Canal
Mountain			Ditch ★

Slopes

Vertical   ⟨Steep⟩   ⟨Gently sloping⟩
⟨Undulating⟩   ⟨Flat⟩

Vegetation

Woodland
Broad-leaved woodland ★★★
Coniferous woodland
Mixed woodland
Scrub ★★

Heathland and grassland
Heather moorland
Upland grass moor
Peat bog
Water meadow
Bracken
Lowland heath
Lowland unimproved grassland ★★

Cultivated land
Arable land ★★★
Improved pasture ★★★
Market gardens and orchards
Parkland

Linear features
Hedgerows ★★★
Woodland fringe ★★
River banks ★
Roadside verges ★★
Railway embankments

Small isolated features
Isolated trees ★
Groups of trees, mainly
broad-leaved
(less than 0.25 ha)
Groups of trees, mainly coniferous
(less than 0.25 ha)
Small shelter-belts ★
Copses and spinneys
Small gardens

Structures

Buildings ★★★	Fences ★
Farmyards	Walls
Camp sites	Telephone wires
Car parks	Electricity pylons
Quarries	Rubbish dumps
Industrial land	Derelict land

1 *Plumpton Wood.* This wood, known as New Wood on an 1841 tithe map, extends to 4.9 hectares. One of four woods on the AWI, it is the only one that has been managed in recent years. Rides were cleared, some conifers planted and a modest amount of coppicing undertaken.

It is roughly rectangular, surrounded by old ditch banks and visible from many parts of the farm. The main entrance to the wood leads roughly northwards through the middle of it; three main east–west rides cross at intervals, one being used as a bridleway through the wood (although it is not marked as such on the Ordnance Survey map). The majority of the trees are standards with hazel coppice, with a diverse ground layer including bluebells. The wide ride provides a pleasant internal landscape (see Figure 2.7). On either side of the entrance is a small plantation of Norway spruce, Scots pine and western red cedar, which is visible only from the south and is not too intrusive; to the east

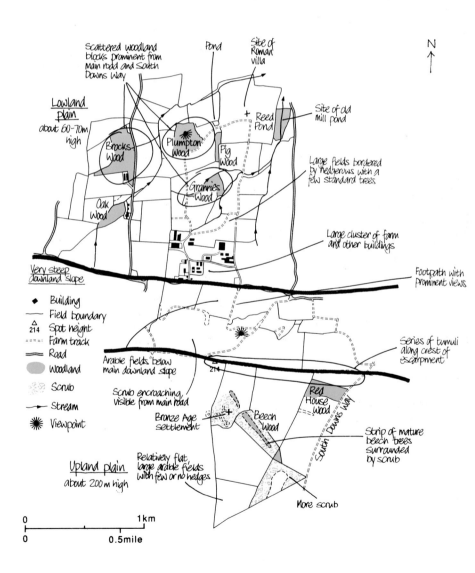

Figure 2.6 Landscape assessment map of the case study farm

30

the growth is tall, the trees never having been thinned; to the west the plantation is a little thin but has been overtaken by naturally regenerating ash.

2   *Reed Pond.* This 2.4 hectare copse appears to be a silted-up catchment area for the two mills downstream, the stream running north–south through the middle of the copse. It is now an even-aged alder copse, less than 100 years old, and has been clear coppiced in the past every 12–13 years. There is a relatively thick understorey of shrubs and many fallen trees and branches. With the wet ground conditions it is difficult to enter, but the open canopy allows a wide range of herb species to grow. There is no public access.

3   *Beech Wood.* This 2.4 hectare wood was planted in the hollow of a valley head on top of the downland escarpment. The beech trees are in two rows about 15 metres apart. Their form of growth suggests they were **pollarded** in their youth. A typical trunk is about 2–3 metres tall at which height the branches radiate like long tendrils in search of light. Beneath is a typical beech wood floor of leaf mould and little else although the area is rich in fungi. The area has also been grazed from time to time. Surrounding the trees, especially to the north-west on the Bronze Age site, are 16 hectares of hawthorn, elder, bracken, bramble and rosebay willow herb scrub of varying density. Being in a hollow the wood is almost hidden from the nearby South Downs Way.

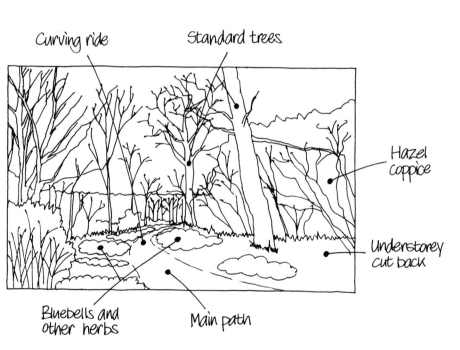

Figure 2.7   Annotated sketch of the main ride in Plumpton Wood

WOODLAND HABITAT ASSESSMENT

Habitat assessment, as described in Chapter 3 of the foundation book, requires at least some understanding of the relationships between species and their habitats. It is also useful to be able to name the plants and animals you find in a habitat (using the many, widely available field guides), to understand how they are likely to react to changes in the habitat, and to recognise the signs that suggest an area may be particularly valuable from a wildlife point of view. In this chapter more detail is given on how these general points can be applied to areas of woodland using the assessment criteria of naturalness, diversity, rarity and size. Because trees are such long-lived features of the environment, their present value as habitat depends to a very large extent on how the woodland has been treated in the past.

3.1 Historical origins

In the absence of human interference, broad-leaved woodland would be the natural **climax community** of lowland areas over much of the country. This means that, where bare ground was colonised by grasses and small herbaceous plants, they would eventually be replaced by shrubs and then by tall trees. Once established, the woodland would remain relatively stable. There might be changes in the dominant tree species over long periods of time, depending on changes in climate and the opportunities for regeneration. For example, some tree seedlings, such as beech and lime, are relatively shade-tolerant and so can compete and grow in the ground layer and eventually invade established woodland. Other seedlings, such as birch and oak, will only thrive where there is a break in the canopy that lets light reach the ground. Birch and oak are good at colonising open ground, but less good at competing with dense herbaceous vegetation. Thus, under natural conditions birch or oak may colonise an area, losing dominance gradually over several hundred years as they are replaced by different species more suited to the new conditions that have developed.

Woodland thus appears to be an unchanging habitat when viewed on a human timescale, but over longer periods of hundreds of years, even under natural conditions, the changes may be dramatic.

Virtually none of the woodland in Great Britain is the untouched natural woodland or wildwood that developed after the last Ice Age. Over the years people either managed or exploited the wildwood itself, or cleared it to grow crops and graze livestock or to build roads or houses. A distinction can still be made between **primary woodland**, occupying sites which have been continuously wooded since the wildwood first developed, and **secondary woodland**, occupying sites which have not been continuously wooded. In the case of secondary woodland, that break in tree cover might have happened as long ago as 500 years, so that being able to distinguish primary woodland from old secondary woodland depends on having access to good historical records.

In practice, it is often more useful to use the historical distinction between ancient and **recent woodland**. Ancient woods are those which originated before AD 1600 and recent woods are those established since then, this being the time when maps and plantation forestry first became important. On this basis, all primary woods are ancient, but the term ancient wood encompasses some secondary as well as primary woodland. The NCC has produced an AWI for most of the country using this definition.

New tree species, not native to this country, have also been introduced to our woodlands over the centuries (see Table 3.1) and many, particularly those that are commercially valuable timber crops, are grown over large areas.

In addition to human interference, British woodland has been shaped by natural catastrophes, particularly **windthrow**, caused by severe gales. Where large areas have been blown down, and natural regeneration has been allowed to take place, the trees will for many years be even-aged, probably with an unbroken canopy. Where single trees or small groups have been blown down or damaged, followed by natural replacement, an uneven-aged stand with a broken canopy will result.

Table 3.1 Native and introduced tree species found or planted in all types of woodland

Native species (in approximate order of arrival)	Introduced species				
	Before 1600	1600–1700	1700–1800	1800–1900	Post-1900
Juniper	Common walnut*	Black walnut	Corsican pine	Beach or shore pine	Commelin elm
Downy birch	Cornish elm	Common lime*	Cricket bat willow*	Douglas fir*	Dawn redwood
Silver birch*	English elm*	Cork oak	Grey alder	Eucalyptus	Hybrid wingnut
Aspen	Grey poplar*	Dutch elm	Lombardy poplar*	Hybrid black poplars*	Raouli*
Scots pine*	Holm oak	European larch*	Red oak*		Roble beech*
Bay willow	Laburnum	False acacia	Turkey oak	Italian alder	
Common alder*	Maritime pine	Horse chestnut*		Japanese larch*	
Hazel	Myrobalan plum	London plane		Lodgepole pine*	
Small-leaved lime*	Norway spruce*	Norway maple*		Red alder	
Bird cherry	Oriental plane	Red maple		Robusta poplar	
Sallow or goat willow*	Smooth-leaved elm*	Scarlet oak		Serbian spruce	
Wych elm*	Stone pine	Sweet gum		Sitka spruce*	
Rowan	Swedish whitebeam	Tulip tree ·		Western balsam poplar	
Sessile oak*	Sweet chestnut*			Western willow	
Ash*	Sycamore*				
Holly*	White poplar*				
Pedunculate or common oak*	Wild pear				
Hawthorn					
Crack willow					
Black poplar					
Yew*					
Whitebeam					
Midland hawthorn					
Crab apple					
Wild cherry*					
White willow					
Field maple					
Wild service tree					
Large-leaved lime*					
Beech*					
Hornbeam*					

(Sources: Evans, 1984; Hibberd, 1986)

* Useful timber trees

There are many areas, particularly on high land in Scotland, where trees were blown down by severe gales in the late nineteenth century and natural regeneration was prevented by sheep-grazing, allowing heather moorland to become the dominant habitat.

3.2   Woodland ecosystems

The value of woodland as a habitat for wildlife depends on many factors such as the age, size and structure of the wood, the soil and climate, and the relationship of the wood to other habitats. These factors determine the range and diversity of the plant and animal species and how they interact with each other and their environment. These interactions or ecological processes, working over many years, shape the woodland ecosystems that we view as the climax to an ecological succession in most areas of the country (Figure 1.4a). These interactions are summarised in Figures 3.1 and 3.2 for deciduous and coniferous woodland ecosystems. The arrows indicate the flow of energy and/or organic material within the woodland community and their relative thicknesses indicate the extent of their influence on the ecosystem.

Soils

The soil type has a strong influence on the woodland ecosystem. A lowland oak wood growing on a relatively mineral-rich 'brown earth' soil has more nutrients available to it than a pine wood growing on a nutrient-deficient 'podsol', which has developed on a hard rock base such as sandstone. Such deficiencies can be because the soil may not have many minerals to begin with, or it may have them in unavailable forms, and/or it loses them through leaching by rainwater. Although there may be fewer herbaceous plant species on the poorer woodland soils of the uplands (they may be rich in mosses) these species are no less valuable.

There are many types of soil, often with names that indicate the rocks or deposits on which they develop. But the main characteristics that typify the soil and what trees or other vegetation do, or may be likely to, grow upon it are texture (heavy or light, clayey or sandy), wetness (dry, wet or waterlogged) and **pH** (acid, neutral or alkaline), as will be seen in Chapters 5 and 6.

Climate

The wetter and cooler climate of the uplands reduces the activities of decomposers and hence limits the flow of nutrients within the ecosystem, leading to the build-up of an acidic plant litter. This litter, especially in coniferous plantations, reduces the opportunities for other plants to establish themselves. The increased acidity also reduces the availability of nutrients. In the drier and warmer lowlands there is often a greater flow of nutrients and a greater rate of decomposition, although there is a strongly seasonal effect in a deciduous woodland. The climate helps determine the distribution of species, for example sessile oak woods are found more in the wetter north and west and pedunculate oak woods in the drier south and east.

Physical structure

The physical features of woodland greatly influence its wildlife. The seasonal changes in deciduous woodland allow more light to reach the woodland floor, encouraging greater variety in the ground flora, whereas conifers provide shade throughout the year. Herbaceous plants depend on the right light

The arrows indicate the relative size of the flow of energy/nutrients

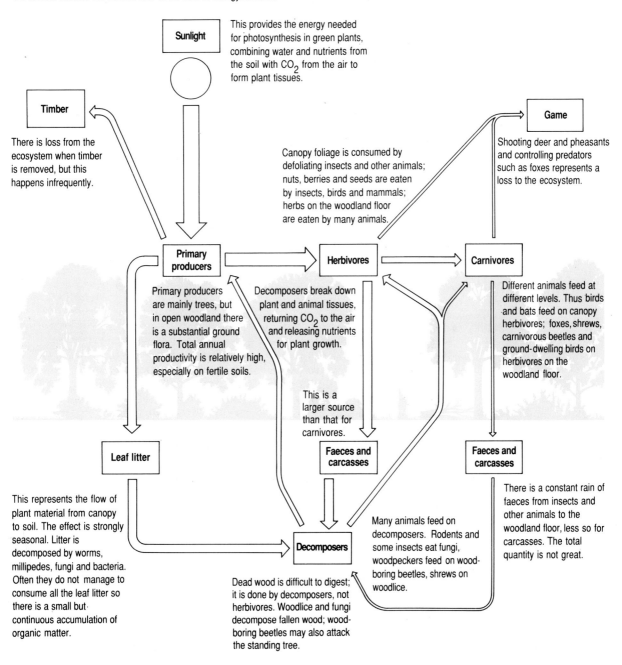

Sunlight

This provides the energy needed for photosynthesis in green plants, combining water and nutrients from the soil with CO_2 from the air to form plant tissues.

Timber

There is loss from the ecosystem when timber is removed, but this happens infrequently.

Canopy foliage is consumed by defoliating insects and other animals; nuts, berries and seeds are eaten by insects, birds and mammals; herbs on the woodland floor are eaten by many animals.

Game

Shooting deer and pheasants and controlling predators such as foxes represents a loss to the ecosystem.

Primary producers

Primary producers are mainly trees, but in open woodland there is a substantial ground flora. Total annual productivity is relatively high, especially on fertile soils.

Herbivores

Decomposers break down plant and animal tissues, returning CO_2 to the air and releasing nutrients for plant growth.

Carnivores

Different animals feed at different levels. Thus birds and bats feed on canopy herbivores; foxes, shrews, carnivorous beetles and ground-dwelling birds on herbivores on the woodland floor.

This is a larger source than that for carnivores.

Leaf litter

This represents the flow of plant material from canopy to soil. The effect is strongly seasonal. Litter is decomposed by worms, millipedes, fungi and bacteria. Often they do not manage to consume all the leaf litter so there is a small but continuous accumulation of organic matter.

Faeces and carcasses

Faeces and carcasses

There is a constant rain of faeces from insects and other animals to the woodland floor, less so for carcasses. The total quantity is not great.

Decomposers

Many animals feed on decomposers. Rodents and some insects eat fungi, woodpeckers feed on wood-boring beetles, shrews on woodlice.

Dead wood is difficult to digest; it is done by decomposers, not herbivores. Woodlice and fungi decompose fallen wood; wood-boring beetles may also attack the standing tree.

Figure 3.1   The deciduous woodland ecosystem. (After Morris, 1980)

The arrows indicate the relative size of the flow of energy/nutrients.

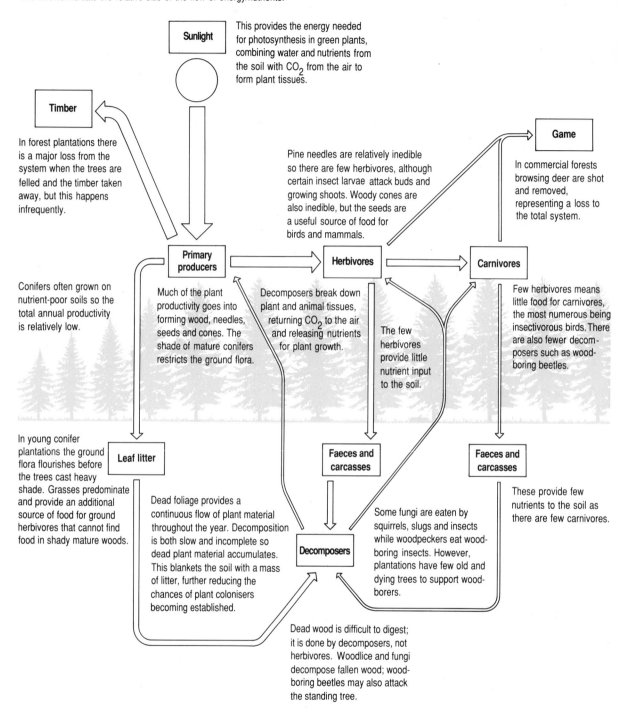

Figure 3.2   The coniferous woodland ecosystem. (After Morris, 1980)

conditions to flourish. Deciduous trees cast shade only from spring until autumn, so in a deciduous woodland there is the opportunity for plants to flower and set seed before being shaded. Breaks in the canopy and the presence of open areas such as glades and rides also favour many woodland butterflies, while different birds thrive at different stages of a woodland's cycle (see Chapter 5).

Ecological types

As different tree species favour different soils and climates, distinct woodland types have developed with a characteristic distribution and association of shrub and herb species. **Semi-natural woodlands** contain mainly native tree species (Table 3.2) which have a greater habitat value than later introductions (Table 3.1). They tend to support more herbivores, and thus often more carnivores, because they have evolved together.

Native trees vary in their natural distribution. Beech, for example, is native to southern England and south-east Wales but not to northern Britain, although it is common there as a planted tree or self-sown from seeds produced by planted trees. Conversely, Scots pine was once native in England and Wales but was naturally replaced by broad-leaved species several thousand years ago and is now regarded as native only in the Scottish Highlands.

Population dynamics

The number and type of plant and animal species found in woodlands change with the seasons and over the years and the populations of consumers and decomposers depend in turn upon the plant and animal species present in the food webs. Generally, a given area of native broad-leaved woodland will contain a greater variety of species of herbivores and decomposers, in greater numbers, than non-native particularly coniferous woodland. This is because native herbivores and decomposers have had a longer period over which to evolve efficient feeding strategies on native plant species and to adapt their life cycles accordingly.

However, like all such generalisations, this one has to be qualified. While it is true that a non-native tree like sycamore will harbour fewer species than a native oak or willow, the actual **biomass** supported, mostly in the form of aphids feeding on the leaves, can be just as great, and these in turn will provide food for carnivorous insects and birds. Also, the structural diversity of the woodland and the openness of the canopy will influence the overall species diversity at least as much as the nature of the dominant tree species. A dense, even-aged stand of beech or even oak can have a relatively low species diversity. It is also important to remember that areas with a poor soil or a harsh climate will almost invariably support woodland with less species diversity than rich lowland soil. In many upland areas, while it is certainly possible to grow broad-leaved trees instead of conifers, and they would probably support a more diverse range of species, they would never produce a commercially viable crop.

Age

The longer an ecosystem has existed, the more time it will have had for new plants and animals to immigrate, become established and evolve new interactions, and the greater the chance that rare and specialised plants and animals will have appeared. Indeed some plant species are treated as indicators

Table 3.2 Classification of semi-natural woodland by stand types, and their areas nationally

Woodland type	Estimated area*
1 Ash–wych elm	
Calcareous ash–wych elm	*****
Wet ash–wych elm	****
Calcareous ash–wych elm on dry and/or heavy soils	**
Western valley ash–wych elm	****
2 Ash–maple	
Wet ash–maple	*****
Ash–maple on light soils	**
Dry ash–maple	**
3 Hazel–ash	
Acid pedunculate oak–hazel–ash	******
Southern calcareous hazel–ash	**
Northern calcareous hazel–ash	***
Acid sessile oak–hazel–ash	***
4 Ash–lime	
Acid birch–ash–lime	***
Maple–ash–lime	**
Sessile oak–ash–lime	**
5 Oak–lime	
Acid pedunculate oak–lime	*****
Acid sessile oak–lime	*****
6 Birch–oak	
Upland sessile oak	******
Upland pedunculate oak	***
Lowland sessile oak	****
Lowland pedunculate oak	******
7 Alder	
Valley alder on mineral soils	*****
Wet valley alder	****
Plateau alder	***
Slope alder	**
Bird cherry–alder	**
8 Beech	
Acid sessile oak–beech	***
Acid pedunculate oak–beech	*****
Calcareous pedunculate oak–ash–beech	****
Acid pedunculate oak–ash–beech	****
Sessile oak–ash–beech	***
9 Hornbeam	
Pedunculate oak–hornbeam	*****
Sessile oak–hornbeam	***
10 Suckering elm	
Invasive elm	****
Valley elm	*
11 Pine	
Acid birch–pine	***
Acid oak–pine	*
Calcareous pine	*
12 Birch	
Rowan–birch	******
Hazel–birch	****

(Source: Peterken, 1985 and personal communication)

* * Less than 200 hectares;
  ** 200 to 2000 hectares;
  *** 2000 to 5000 hectares;
  **** 5000 to 10 000 hectares;
  ***** 10 000 to 25 000 hectares;
  ****** more than 25 000 hectares.

of ancient woodland because they are usually only found in these relatively stable, long-lived ecosystems. Although some indicator species occur in other habitats and not in every ancient woodland, the more of them that are present, the greater the wildlife value of the woodland is likely to be (see Appendix III of the foundation book).

Indicator species vary in their usefulness in different parts of the country, being more valuable at the margins of their ranges.

3.3　Woodland habitat assessment criteria

With a basic understanding of woodland ecology, as described in Section 3.2, a detailed assessment of the wildlife habitat value of woodland can be made. This can never be truly 'objective'. There will always be situations where even experts will disagree, or cases where personal preferences have an important influence, but, as with other habitats, the following criteria are a useful general guide to a wood's wildlife value:

▷ its naturalness;

▷ its diversity;

▷ its rarity and the rarity of the species it contains;

▷ its area or size.

As with landscape assessment, assessing the wildlife value of woodland is best done by marking important areas on a map, taking photographs or making sketches from recorded positions and making detailed notes describing each area.

If the site has been designated, for example as an SSSI, detailed surveys will already have been made by professional naturalists from the NCC and a copy given to the landowner. Even so it is a good idea to do your own assessment too as you will learn more about the area, and be able to take a more constructive part in its management in future.

Naturalness

Although we value naturalness in a habitat more highly than artificiality, no British woodland could be described with certainty as 'natural'. It has all been modified by human activity in some way, by management for timber, firewood, fencing, game or grazing animals. The most natural (and thus most highly valued) areas remaining today are those described as 'ancient semi-natural woodland', areas that have been continuously wooded since about AD 1600 or earlier, when maps first became widely available and plantation forestry first became widely practised. Some such sites may have been continuously wooded since the primeval forest covered the country. Others, even if clear felled at some time, have been in existence for long enough to have acquired ecological communities similar to those in primary woodland. In addition to the broad-leaved ancient semi-natural woodland characteristic of lowland areas, there are a few remnants in the Scottish Highlands of the ancient Caledonian forest, predominantly of Scots pine. Woodland or forest created since 1600 tends to be progressively less 'natural'.

As outlined above, another factor that contributes to the degree of naturalness in woodland is the extent to which it consists of native rather than non-native

Table 3.3 Habitat assessment criteria for woodland

Criterion	Rating
1 Naturalness	
Ancient semi-natural woodland	★★★★
Recent woodland, predominantly native species	★★★
Recent woodland, mixed native and non-native species	★★
Recent woodland, predominantly non-native species, with some native species at the woodland edge and along rides	★
2 Diversity	
2.1 Plant species diversity per transect (30 minute walk) in woods on alkaline and neutral soils	
More than 30 species	★★★★
Between 21 and 30 species	★★★
Between 11 and 20 species	★★
Less than 10 species	★
2.2 Plant species diversity per transect (30 minute walk) in woods on acid soils	
More than 15 species	★★★★
Between 11 and 15 species	★★★
Between 6 and 10 species	★★
Less than 5 species	★
2.3 Structural diversity	
Uneven-aged wood with open canopy and well developed tree, shrub, herb and ground layers	★★★★
Even-aged wood with open canopy and well developed tree, shrub, herb and ground layers	★★★
Uneven-aged wood with open canopy and poorly developed or grazed herb and ground layers	★★
Even-aged wood with closed canopy and poorly developed shrub, herb and ground layers	★
3 Rarity	
3.1 Habitat rarity	
Nationally rare	★★★★
Regionally rare	★★★
Regionally common but not nationally	★★
Nationally and regionally common	★
3.2 Species rarity	
Containing one (or more) species of plant and/or animal that is nationally rare	★★★★
Containing one (or more) species of plant and/or animal that is locally or regionally rare	★★★
Containing plant and/or animal species that are widespread, but restricted to woodland habitat	★★
Containing no species in any of the above categories	★
4 Area	
Woodland that does not score more than ★ for naturalness, diversity or rarity, regardless of size	0
Woodland more than 10 ha	★★★★
Woodland between 5 and 10 ha	★★★
Woodland between 2 and 5 ha	★★
Woodland less than 2 ha	★

or introduced species (see Table 3.1). Many recent plantations consist of non-native species but some woods have species mixtures planted to mimic the associations found naturally in the same region (see Table 3.2) or have developed by natural regeneration and so would rate quite highly on the naturalness scale.

Detailed inventories of ancient woodlands in Great Britain are kept in the regional offices of the NCC and by county councils (see Figure 3.3d). Historical and archaeological evidence of ancient woodland includes the presence of raised banks and/or boundaries that follow parish boundaries, as indicated on some 1:25 Ordnance Survey maps or older maps, deeds or documents (see Chapter 2). Other clues to the naturalness of a woodland lie in the presence of representative species in the ground flora of the wood (see Appendix III of the foundation book). Table 3.3 indicates how you could rate woodland for naturalness.

Diversity

Species diversity

Diversity in one sense is a measure of the variety of plant and animal species found in a habitat. Usually older woodland will be more diverse than more recent woodland, simply because it has had a longer time to be colonised. However, some recent woodlands may have been deliberately planted with a wider range of species, or allowed to regenerate naturally, and will therefore have a relatively high species diversity. Alternatively, species diversity may have been created by management practices such as selective felling and replanting.

Because animals depend directly or indirectly on plants for their existence, the greater the diversity of plants in a habitat, the greater the diversity of animals in most cases. It is therefore possible, and simpler, to score the woodland only on the basis of its plant diversity.

You should make this assessment at a time of year when most plants are clearly recognisable, such as late spring for most flowering plants, bushes and trees and autumn for fungi. If you are going to assess the diversity several years in succession, so as to make comparisons, remember to do it at the same time each year. Comparison from one year to the next, or between one area and another, will also not be possible unless you adopt a standard procedure, such as counting all the species you see in a 30 minute walk through the wood, following as straight a line as possible. See Table 3.3 for an indication of how to score woodland for species diversity.

It is not essential to be able to name accurately all the species you find, so long as you can remember which ones you have already counted. If you are making a list, you could use a short description instead of the name, e.g. 'yellow, shiny, star-shaped flower with heart-shaped leaf' for lesser celandine, or include a rough sketch. However, if you are to take an interest in land management you will find it invaluable to know the names of at least the commoner species in your area. Do not pick or dig up plants as some are protected by law (see the *Legislation and Regulations* booklet). And don't forget to include the tree species in your list!

Structural diversity

The second sense of diversity that needs to be considered is structural diversity. Woodland that has a relatively open canopy with a well-developed **understorey**, field layer and ground layer will support a greater variety of

41

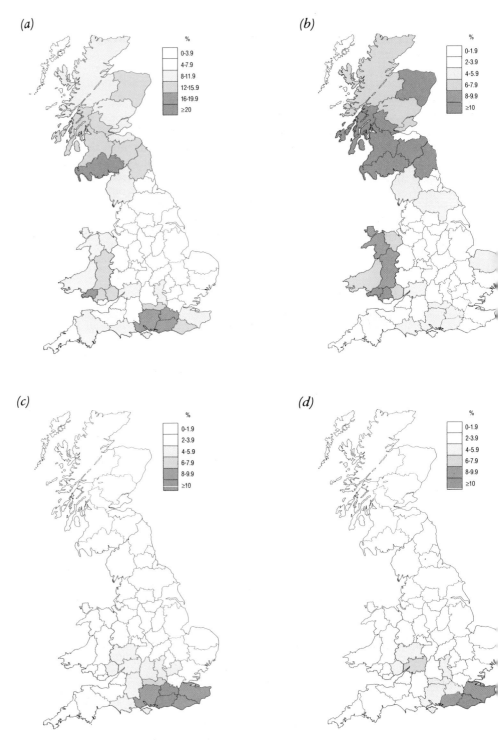

Figure 3.3 Woodlands as a percentage of total land area (counties in England and Wales, regions in Scotland): (a) total woodland area including forests (after Locke, 1987); (b) mainly coniferous high forest area (after Locke, 1987); (c) mainly broad-leaved woodland area (after Locke, 1987); (d) ancient woodland area (NCC, 1989, personal communication)

species overall. This structural diversity may have occurred in a variety of ways:

- by felling and replanting small areas in rotation;
- by opening up wide rides and glades within the wood;
- by managing as coppice or coppice-with-standards;
- by coppicing or felling only a proportion of the wood at any one time;
- by leaving small areas that blow down to regenerate naturally;
- by cutting back mature trees at the woodland edge to allow a gradation in vegetation height.

Some of the woodland that was coppiced in the past is now being allowed to revert to high forest. You can recognise overgrown coppice by the presence of many trees with several stems arising from the same root. These could be **singled** to produce commercially viable high forest. If coppiced again in future, such areas may develop a diverse ground flora because of the reservoir of seed built up in the soil at a time when coppicing was more common, but such seed banks only survive for about 30 years.

Structural diversity may have been reduced by very close planting of trees, which has prevented light from reaching the lower layers of the woodland. On the other hand, where animals are allowed to graze under trees without restriction, the herb and ground vegetation layers will become impoverished, even when the canopy is relatively open. Under these circumstances, natural regeneration is prevented, the existing trees will eventually become over-mature and die, and the woodland will disappear. (Light grazing is of course a natural part of the woodland ecosystem.)

The structural diversity of woodland thus applies to both the vertical and the horizontal structure of the wood and to the relative ages of the different compartments, an uneven-aged wood effectively creating an open canopy. Table 3.3 shows how to rate woodland for structural diversity.

Rarity

The term rarity can refer both to species and to habitats. Ancient semi-natural woodland is now a rare habitat in Great Britain and is therefore very highly valued. Because of the rarity of the habitat, many of the species that depend on it have also become rare, for example the one-flowered wintergreen of native pine woods in north-east Scotland, or the yellow archangel of the English lowlands. Other species found in ancient woodland are much less restricted in their habitat requirements and are therefore still quite common, for example the primrose.

Habitat rarity

To assess the habitat rarity of woodland, you need to consider first whether it is nationally rare; for example, ancient semi-natural broad-leaved woodland or a remnant of the Caledonian Scots pine forest, which would be given the highest rating. An indication of habitat rarity can be based on the relative areas of certain woodland types with distinctive associations of shrub and herb species, as shown in Table 3.2. In some parts of the country woodland habitat of any age is rare, as in parts of East Anglia. In such cases, any woodland, regardless of its age, would rate quite highly. Where woodland is common, and your particular area of woodland is not ancient, it would not rate very highly on this criterion, although it may do so on others (see Table 3.3).

43

The presence of rare species in woodland often indicates that it is ancient, so that they, along with more common species, are referred to as 'indicator' or 'representative' species. However, rare species do occur in woodland that is not ancient if it has been allowed to develop or been managed so as to encourage them.

Table 3.3 shows how you can grade woodland on the basis of the number of rare species it contains although you have to be able to identify the species. Late spring is the ideal time to do such an assessment, when plants and animals are most visible and most easily recognised, but ideally you should survey the woodland at several times during the growing season. If you are at all uncertain about the rarity value of your woodland or the species it contains, contact a professional biologist or a competent amateur naturalist. Members of local nature conservation or wildlife trusts are usually willing to help (see the *Helpful Organisations* booklet).

Area

If a piece of woodland is rated highly for naturalness, diversity and/or rarity, then obviously the bigger the area, the better its value for wildlife. The larger predatory animals and birds, such as hawks, owls, pine martens or wild cats, need large territories to provide them with enough food. They will therefore not be able to survive in a small area of isolated woodland. They may be able to survive in areas where many small patches of woodland occur close together, so the extent to which the surrounding area is well-wooded is very important.

If the area of woodland is large, it is less likely that some of its species will be totally wiped out by a natural catastrophe such as a very cold winter. In larger areas, a few individuals are more likely to survive and replenish the breeding stock. In well-wooded areas (Figure 3.3), there will be enough movement between different patches to prevent local extinctions of species that disperse easily.

If the woodland in an area scores poorly on the other three criteria, then a larger area probably will not justify a higher score. For example, if you are dealing with a closely planted monoculture of coniferous forest, a large area could be worse from a wildlife point of view than a small area, particularly if it displaced another, more valuable habitat.

The scoring of woodland habitats on the basis of area is summarised in Table 3.3.

3.4 Overall woodland habitat assessment

The four habitat assessment criteria described above overlap to some extent: a wood that has a high score for one criterion is more likely to have a high score for the others and vice versa. However, they do not overlap completely: a wood may have a high score for species diversity but a low score for rarity. Remember that the ratings are not quantitative and should not be treated like real numbers – a wood that rates four stars on naturalness cannot be considered twice as good as one that rates two stars. Nor need you obtain a rating for each criterion if it is difficult, although the more you have the better.

How do you rate the quality of this establishment?

THE OLD SETT

Taken together, ratings of your woodland from the checklist in Table 3.3 provide an overview of its habitat value and a basis for improving it. You can then look at individual or related criteria to see what can be done to improve them without downgrading the woodland on the remaining criteria. For example, an area of highly valued ancient woodland may be only 5 hectares in area and could be improved by encouraging natural colonisation and regeneration in adjoining land. The structural and species diversity of an even-aged plantation could be improved by selective felling and/or the opening up of glades and rides. The overall objectives should be *to maintain* those aspects of woodland that are already highly rated, *to enhance* those that are of poor to moderate value and *to create* new features that will add to its value.

3.5   *Making your own woodland habitat assessment*

As with landscapes, this is a more specific extension of the general habitat assessment described in Chapter 3 of the foundation book and shown for the case studies in Section 3.6.

Fill in a general habitat assessment profile for your holding, concentrating on the areas of woodland (or one for each distinct area if there is more than one). Supplement this with more detail on the woodland criteria, as suggested in Table 3.3, using a checklist like the one shown in Tables 3.5 and 3.7, adding the main reasons for the rating in the notes and comments column.

Table 3.4 Habitat assessment profile

Land holding *Killiehangie Wood*   Habitat type   *Woodland*   Habitat number
Date *4/5/89*

A *Physical features*

1 Land use: Past uses *Forestry for over 100 years, probably farmland previously*
                 Present uses *Forestry*

2 Physical conditions:

See Figure 2.2

Terrain   flat, sloping, undulating *Undulating with gentle slopes and steep crags*
Age   <5 years, 5–10 years, (10–50 years) >50 years
Area   <0.5 ha, 0.5–1 ha, 1–5 ha, (>5 ha)
Soil wetness   (well drained) occasionally waterlogged, always waterlogged
Soil texture   silty, (sandy) clayey
Soil chemistry (acidic,) neutral, alkaline

B *Wildlife features*

1 Vegetation cover
   (∗ = present; ∗∗ = moderately common; ∗∗∗ = frequent)

   Mosses ∗ ∗   Grasses ∗ ∗   Shrubs ∗
   Ferns ∗   Herbs ∗ ∗   Trees ∗ ∗ ∗

2 Animals
   (∗ = present; ∗∗ = moderately common; ∗∗∗ = frequent)

   Insects ∗ ∗   Amphibians   Birds ∗ ∗ ∗
   Molluscs   Reptiles ∗   Mammals ∗ ∗

3 Habitat assessment criteria
   (∗ = low value; ∗∗ = moderate value; ∗∗∗ = high value)

   Diversity ∗ ∗   Naturalness ∗
   Rarity ∗   Area ∗ ∗ ∗

C *Land use features*
   (∗ = low value; ∗∗ = moderate value; ∗∗∗ = high value)

   Wildlife ∗ ∗   Education ∗ ∗ ∗   Forestry ∗ ∗ ∗
   Recreation ∗ ∗   Agriculture ∗   Industry ∗

D *Summary assessment*   *see notes in Section 3.6*   46

3.6 Habitat assessment of case study areas

Killiehangie Hill, Atholl Estate

Table 3.4 shows a habitat assessment profile of the woodland on Killiehangie
Hill and Table 3.5 shows the woodland habitat checklist. The habitat
assessment was done only on the area of intensively managed, largely
coniferous forest, this being the area currently suffering from a management
problem due to red deer damage. The forest manager walked in a relatively
straight line for approximately 30 minutes, crossing several woodland tracks
and rides.

The habitat is typical of many areas of upland coniferous forest, except
perhaps for the presence of two SSSIs, both ponds and invisible from outside
the wood. The only management constraints are to ensure that trees do not
shade the ponds excessively and to maintain a reasonable amount of open
water.

Despite its low ratings for naturalness, structural diversity and habitat and
species rarity, there is a surprisingly large number of plant species. This
indicates the benefits that can be obtained from opening up rides and glades
within the wood and encouraging natural vegetation on small areas that fail or
are too steep or rocky to be planted.

The rocky crags, which are outside the area being considered in detail here (see
Figure 2.2), are an attractive area for wildlife and birch, willow, larch, rowan
and ash are colonising the area naturally in small pockets of soil. There are
scattered remnants of large Scots pine on the hillside that have been left to
grow naturally.

Table 3.5 Woodland habitat checklist for Killiehangie Hill

Date 4/5/89

Criterion		Rating*	Notes and comments
1	Naturalness	✳	
2	Diversity		Acid woodland: 41 species counted, including 12 trees, 2 mosses and 3 grasses, chiefly on ride sides, extraction clearings and rocky areas.
	2.1 Species	✳✳✳✳	But still contained 41 plant species
	2.2 Structural	✳	
3	Rarity		
	3.1 Habitat	✳	
	3.2 Species	✳✳	
4	Area	✳✳✳✳	

* See Table 3.3.

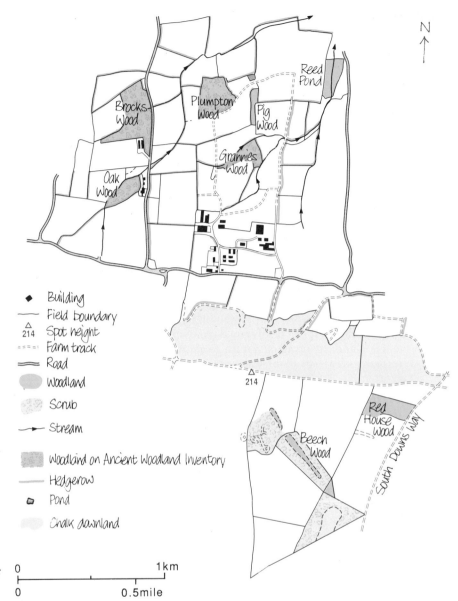

Figure 3.4   Habitat assessment for the Sussex case study farm

In the middle slope zone the greatest scope for improvement in the wildlife habitat value of this forest lies with the criteria of naturalness and structural diversity. Although the total number of plant species is quite high the proportion of the forest area occupied by natural habitat is very low and the commercial forest consists almost entirely of a single species, of uniform age structure.

Small woods in Sussex

(Please note that this is not comprehensive and concentrates on the major features.)

Whole farm

The farm has a wide variety of wildlife habitats (Figure 3.4), including:

▶ 28 hectares of woodland including almost 15 hectares classified as ancient woodland;

Table 3.6 Habitat assessment profile

Land holding _Sussex Case Study Farm_ Habitat type _Woodland_ Habitat number _Plumpton Wood_ Date _May 1989_

A *Physical features*

1 Land use: Past uses
Present uses } _Woodland_

2 Physical conditions:

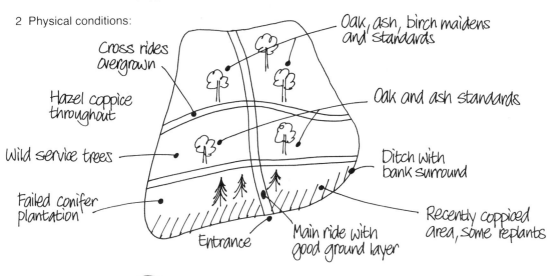

Cross rides overgrown

Oak, ash, birch maidens and standards

Hazel coppice throughout

Oak and ash standards

Wild service trees

Ditch with bank surround

Failed conifer plantation

Recently coppiced area, some replants

Entrance

Main ride with good ground layer

Terrain	(flat,) sloping, undulating
Age	<5 years, 5–10 years, 10–50 years, (>50 years)
Area	<0.5 ha, 0.5–1 ha, (1–5 ha,) >5 ha
Soil wetness	well drained, (occasionally waterlogged,) always waterlogged
Soil texture	silty, sandy, (clayey)
Soil chemistry	acidic, (neutral,) (alkaline)

B *Wildlife features*

1 Vegetation cover
   (* = present; ** = moderately common; *** = frequent)

Mosses **	Grasses **	Shrubs ***
Ferns *	Herbs ***	Trees ***

2 Animals
   (* = present; ** = moderately common; *** = frequent)

Insects ***	Amphibians	Birds ***
Molluscs	Reptiles	Mammals **

3 Habitat assessment criteria
   (* = low value; ** = moderate value; *** = high value)

Diversity	Naturalness	}
Rarity	Area	See Table 3.8

C *Land use features*
   (* = low value; ** = moderate value; *** = high value)

Wildlife ***	Education **	Forestry *
Recreation *	Agriculture	Industry

D *Summary assessment* _See notes in Section 3.6_

▶ several kilometres of hedgerows, 74% estimated to be over 400 years old and 48% over 500 years old;

▶ two main streams of varying quality, one having been polluted by farm waste in the past;

▶ a badly silted pond that has been dredged recently;

▶ a large area of natural grassland which has suffered in the past from erosion by overwintering cattle and from hawthorn and elder scrub invasion due to discontinued sheep grazing and reduction of rabbit numbers through myxomatosis;

▶ a substantial area of scrub surrounding Beech Wood.

Woodland areas

The woodland on the farm divides up into the ancient woods, for example Plumpton Wood, and the recent woods, for example Reed Pond and Beech Wood. The former are particularly rich in plants and insects, the latter much less so. There is a variety of birds in all the woods, at least 32 species and 141 pairs being recorded in one year, including great spotted woodpecker, goldcrest, long-tailed tit, nuthatch and treecreeper.

Plumpton Wood is a very valuable habitat, as shown by the habitat assessment profile (Table 3.6) and the habitat checklist (Table 3.7). It contains an interesting transition between two woodland types and has quite a rich ground flora, including dog's mercury, bluebell, wood anemone, yellow archangel, enchanter's nightshade and ramsons. Of particular note are a few wild service trees. Table 3.7 also shows ratings for Reed Pond and Beech Wood for comparison. Beech Wood in particular does not score well and is in most need of enhancement.

Table 3.7 Woodland habitat checklist for (a) Plumpton Wood; (b) Reed Pond; (c) Beech Wood

Date   May 1989

Criterion		Rating*	
	(a)	(b)	(c)
1 Naturalness	✳✳✳✳	✳✳✳	✳✳✳
2 Diversity			
2.1 Species	✳✳✳✳	✳✳	✳
2.2 Structural	✳✳✳✳	✳✳	✳✳
3 Rarity			
3.1 Habitat	✳✳	✳✳✳	✳✳
3.2 Species	✳✳✳✳✳	✳✳	✳✳
4 Area	✳✳	✳✳	✳✳

* See Table 3.3.

Chapter 4

BUSINESS AND INTEGRATED ASSESSMENT

In this chapter you will be shown how to assess the current commercial or business value of woodland on a holding, how these interact with the landscape and conservation interests, and how the various assessments may be integrated.

Much woodland in Britain is managed commercially for timber production, for use in buildings and other structures and for furniture, fencing materials and wood pulp. Wood is also used as a fuel, but much less so than in the past when commoners had the right to collect firewood, and charcoal-burning supported industries such as iron-making. Currently there is renewed interest in planting fast-growing trees as fuel for wood-burning stoves and open fires.

Woodland has also been used for grazing animals, when it is known as **wood-pasture**. Trees in wood-pasture were traditionally managed and rejuvenated by pollarding, a process similar to coppicing, where trees are cut in rotation about 2 metres above the ground, so that the fresh new growth is out of the reach of grazing animals. Some woods have common grazing rights, although these were reduced in number by the Acts of Enclosure. Other wood-pastures were often developed as deer **parks**. Interest in wood-pasture is currently being revived under the name of **agroforestry**, a term which includes silvopastoral (trees in pasture) and silvoarable (trees in arable crops) systems.

Woodlands may also be managed for rearing game and to sustain field sports. Apart from deer parks, many **coverts** and copses on farms and estates are used for raising pheasants. Indeed, gamekeepers often see woods only in terms of rearing grounds for their game animals.

Some woods have been planted purely for amenity, landscape or recreational purposes, while many existing woods are crossed by footpaths or are the focus of activity for a local community. Several outdoor pursuits are also bringing people into woods and forests.

4.1 Business assessment

When you are assessing the commercial value or potential of an area of woodland, timber production will probably be the first consideration that comes to mind. But remember that the site may present other opportunities, such as fuel wood production or management for game or for tourism.

Just as an entire holding can be divided into landscape zones, it is very useful from a management point of view to divide woodland areas into **compartments**. For a small wood with a fairly uniform structure the compartment may consist of the whole wood. However, if some areas are distinctively different from others, and would therefore be managed differently, even a small wood could usefully be divided into two or more compartments. In larger areas of woodland the compartment number provides the main reference for all management operations. Here the boundaries of compartments tend to follow features that are easily identifiable on the

Dividing woodland into compartments

51

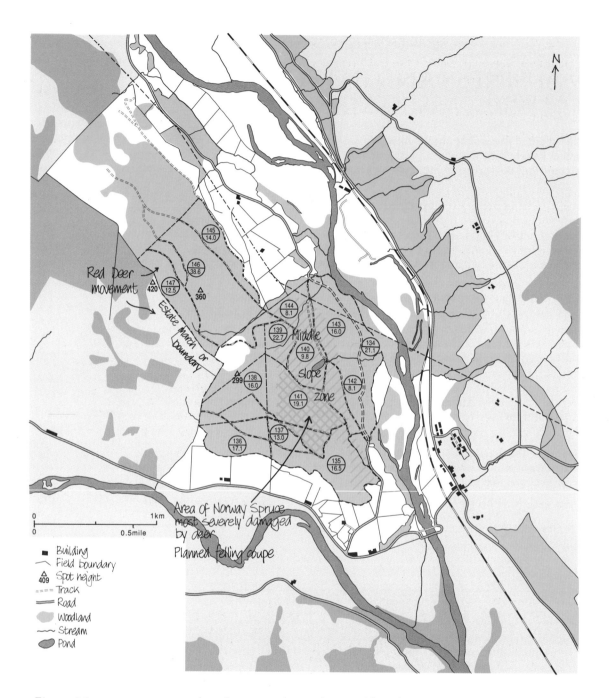

Inside the figure:

N

145 / 14.0

146 / 38.6

Red Deer movement
420
147 / 12.5
360

Estate March or Boundary

144 / 8.1

143 / 16.0

139 / 22.7
Middle

140 / 9.8

134 / 21.1

299
138 / 16.0
Slope

141 / 19.1
zone

142 / 8.1

137 / 13.0

136 / 17.1

135 / 16.5

Area of Norway Spruce most severely damaged by deer

Planned felling coupe

0 ___ 1km
0 ___ 0.5mile

■ Building
⌐ Field boundary
△ 409 Spot height
==== Track
══ Road
Woodland
～ Stream
◯ Pond

*Figure 4.1
Management
compartments for
Killiehangie Hill*

ground, such as streams, roadways, rides, changes in species mix and fire-breaks. For example, in Figure 4.1, showing Killiehangie Hill, each set of numbers enclosed in a circle indicates the compartment number (top number) and the area in hectares (bottom number).

The terms 'stand' and 'compartment' are sometimes used interchangeably, although 'stand' is much less precise. A stand usually means a naturally-defined area of trees, often delineated by landscape features, and one stand may be divided into several compartments for management purposes.

Timber and fuel wood production

Assessing the cropping potential of woodland is much the same as for any other crop. The key questions are:

- what is the crop;
- what stage of growth is it at;
- how good is its quality;
- is it accessible;
- what will it yield and when (the rotation)?

However, the simplicity of these questions is deceptive. Applying yield assessment to crop valuation can be very misleading and training and experience are needed. It could be said that the only true valuation of a crop is the best offer you receive when offering it for standing sale! This brief section can give you only a general idea of the processes involved. You can learn more about the subject by joining the Royal Scottish Forestry Society or Royal Forestry Society of England, Wales and Northern Ireland who run regular excursions where you can discuss these matters, and where contacts can be made with marketing and other useful organisations. When valuing woodland, always get two or three quotations in order to compare prices.

What is the crop?

You need to know what tree species are present in an area of woodland as some species are much more valuable commercially than others. A given volume of well-grown broad-leaved **sawlogs** is usually more valuable than its coniferous counterpart, but this will depend to some extent on the availability of a local market. You also have to take account of the fact that broad-leaves grow more slowly than conifers. If there is no local market for poorer quality hardwoods such as oak, beech or ash, selling them cheaply for firewood may be an option. However, lorries will travel the length and breadth of Britain to collect *good* quality **hardwood** logs even in small quantities.

What stage of growth is it at?

The stages of growth can be summarised as follows:

- weeding stage (establishment);
- cleaning stage (establishment);
- **thicket** or pre-thinning stage;
- thinning stage;
- felling or mature stage.

In Box 4.1 the activities at each of these stages are summarised. Some silvicultural systems such as selection forestry and shelter-wood systems may have some or all of the stages in one stand; in plantation forestry they are usually separate. It is important to recognise the stages in order to plan future essential work and for budgeting purposes. Equally important is to know when to leave well alone, say for 5 years, except for keeping a watching brief. The age and therefore the likely growth stage of an area of woodland should be known from woodland records and the planting date. If these are not available then rough estimates will have to be made, based on tree size, as described below.

How good is its quality?

The quality of the timber is reflected in the value of the crop. The value of a stand of timber is decided by both quality and volume together with quality of access. Profitability depends additionally on the growth rate and the establishment and management costs. Poor commercial quality woodland or scrub has a poor stocking of marketable species, other than for firewood, with many defective or diseased trees. However, this does not imply that the

Box 4.1   Stages of growth of a timber crop

Weeding stage

First 3 or 4 years after planting. The action needed is to prevent trees becoming suppressed by bracken, grass and other weeds. Weeds can be cut by sharp-edged tools or controlled chemically. In hot dry spells it is sometimes beneficial to the crop to defer weeding, and over-weeding can expose plants to deer damage in certain instances.

Cleaning stage

Approximately 5–7 years after planting. **Cleaning** is the term used for cutting out invading species such as birch, unwanted coppice growth and honeysuckle. At this stage it is important to decide whether you wish to accept some of these invading species into the crop to increase the species diversity. It will benefit the conservation value of the woodland if you allow this where possible.

Thicket or pre-thinning stage

Approximately 10–18 years after planting. This is the time to 'shut the forest gate'; to keep a watch for pests, disease and vermin attack and to let the trees grow. **Brashing** may be done just before thinning.

Thinning stage

This is when some trees are removed to give growing space to the remainder. The stand starts to produce income and this is also referred to as the production stage, starting from about 15 to 25 years after planting, depending on species. A subject on its own, this is the stage which determines the future appearance and structure of the stand, particularly in the case of mixed plantings.

Felling or mature stage

At this period the crop is ready for felling, the growth rate has been slowing down for several years but the declining increment is often being added to trees which, because of their size and quality, have now moved into a higher price range. So it is important to consider the cash value of the crop, and the rate at which this is increasing, rather than just the tonnage. The optimum felling age in coniferous crops is related more straightforwardly to tonnage than in broad-leaved stands where the price increment for size and quality is more marked.

woodland is unsatisfactory for other purposes such as landscape, amenity, conservation or sporting uses.

Trees grow at very different rates, depending on the species, soil and climate and, except in the case of thinnings, harvesting good quality trees before they are mature would generally be a waste of a valuable resource. Table 4.1 gives the approximate relationship between the age of commercially valuable species and their diameter at breast height (**dbh**), the most convenient measure of tree size. Tape measures are available that have been specially calibrated to give a direct reading of dbh when they are passed round the circumference of the tree. These are known as 'girth tapes' or 'diameter tapes'. Alternatively, you can use an ordinary tape measure and divide the figure obtained for the circumference by 3.14 to give the diameter. It is usually worthwhile to measure the girth of all trees over 30 centimetres dbh, but only a representative sample of smaller trees. A more accurate but somewhat drastic measure can be obtained by felling a tree and counting the annual rings.

Table 4.2 shows the diameter specifications required for various end-uses of the timber.

Table 4.1 Relationship of tree size (diameter) to age (years from planting) for different species*

Species	Age at which tree reaches a dbh (cm) of:					
	10	20	30	40	50	60+
Beech	35	55	75	95	115	140
Oak	30	50	70	90	120	150
Ash, sycamore, cherry, walnut	20	30	40	60	–	–
Alder, birch	15	25	35	–	–	–
Pine	20	40	60	80	–	–
Spruce	25	40	55	80	–	–
Larch	15	30	45	70	–	–

(Source: MAFF, 1986)

*Ages shown are averages, i.e. what might be expected on reasonably drained, poor quality land; both much faster and much slower growth can occur depending on the site. Also, in every stand, some trees grow faster and some grow slower than average.

The density of planting will also affect the type of tree growth. Close spacing results in tall slender trees, open spacing in greater girth and coarse branches. Table 4.3 shows the normal spacing (or planting density) for trees of various sizes and also the conditions of understocking and overstocking. If the density of your stand is greater than normal, it should probably be thinned. If the density is considerably less than normal, additional trees could be planted, provided that you decided to develop the stand for timber production. Shade-tolerant trees such as beech or silver fir will be most likely to succeed when planted into an existing stand. Trees planted in an open site will grow up to 50% faster than those grown in closed-canopy woodland but the total timber production from the area planted will often be less.

A vigorously growing stand will reach maturity faster than a slow-growing one. Most conifers are considered mature when they are 40–80 years old, 20–25 metres high and 30–40 centimetres dbh. Trees like oak and beech should be at least 100 years old and 50 centimetres dbh before they are considered commercially mature, although over-maturity may not occur until they are 150–200 years old.

Factors which can affect quality include disease, fungal and insect attack, rabbit and deer damage, stem form, growth rate and natural factors such as **shake** and staining. Special 'value-adding' features, for example veneer quality wood with rare markings, can be recognised by specialists who will also know where to sell such timber.

Good quality timber is generally straight-grained and free from knots. This means that the stems should be straight and free from branching below about 6 metres for conifers or less for some broad-leaved trees – down to 2.5 metres for veneer oak or sycamore. Quality variation in hardwoods is much greater than in **softwoods**, making hardwood values much more difficult for the amateur to estimate.

Disease in woodland usually affects only occasional trees or small groups of them, leading to symptoms such as crown dieback, the presence of fungal brackets on the stem, premature loss or yellowing of the leaves, or liquid or resin oozing from the bark. If you want to develop a stand of trees presently showing symptoms of disease or insect attack for timber production you should consult an expert forester.

Table 4.2 Diameter specifications for various end-uses

Product	Diameter over bark (cm)	Comments
	10 20 30 40 50 60+	
Firewood	——————— – – –	
Pulpwood	———————	White woods preferred
Turnery:		
alder, birch, maple, sycamore	——— – – –	
ash, beech	——— – – –	
Fencing:		
sawn	——— – – –	Mainly oak
cleft/round	——— – – –	Mainly sweet chestnut
Mining timber (sawn)	——————— – –	Mainly oak
Prime timber:		
planking/furniture/joinery	– – – – – ——— – – –	If good quality, smaller sizes of ash and beech usable
high class joinery	——— – – – –	Mainly cherry/walnut
Veneer (ornamental):		
cherry/walnut	– – – ——— – – –	
ash/sycamore/ sweet chestnut	——— – – –	
oak/elm	——— –	
Miscellaneous:		
sports ash	——————— – – –	Must be white
peeled poplar for crates	——————— – – –	

(Source: Evans, 1984)

Table 4.3 Stocking density of trees of various sizes

Average diameter of trees (cm)	Overstocked – trees too close if:		Normal stocking density if:		Understocked – trees too far apart if:		Grossly understocked – far too few trees if:	
	Spacing (m) less than	Trees/ha more than	Spacing (m)	Trees/ha	Spacing (m) more than	Trees/ha less than	Spacing (m) more than	Trees/ha less than
<10*	1.5	4500	1.5–3	1200–4000	3	1000	5	500
10–20	2	2500	2.5–3.5	800–1700	4	600	6	300
20–30	3	1100	4–6	300–600	7	200	10	100
30–40	4	600	5–7	200–400	9	120	12	70
40–50	5	400	6–8	150–300	10	100	14	50
50–60	7	200	8–10	100–150	12	70	16	40
>65	8	150	10–14	50–100	16	40	20	25

(Source: MAFF, 1986)   * Newly planted or regenerated.

Access

Many small areas of woodland suffer from poor access which greatly increases the cost of harvesting the crop. Access quality depends on the ground conditions and the vehicle available for extraction. Wood is removed from the felling point (at stump) by skidding (dragging along the ground using winch tractors) or using a **forwarder** (it is lifted onto a wheeled trailer by a mounted grip loader). Hilly sites may have three extraction methods – a skyline or high cable crane, then ground skidding followed by forwarding. Distance is an important consideration for ground skidding, but much less so with forwarding where, once logs are loaded, several hundred yards can be covered in a matter of minutes. A firewood merchant working on a small scale might use a landrover or dumper truck to avoid using tractors which often cause serious damage to rides.

The relationship between timber value and extraction costs can vary. A **pulpwood** crop may be uneconomical if access is poor and prices are low, but a rise in prices could make it profitable, even with poor access. At the other extreme, a valuable parcel of sawlogs can often stand the extra costs imposed by poor access. You should check whether any firm quoting for your timber has taken access into account.

Most owners of small woods will want to bring in a contractor to harvest the timber when it is mature and this is unlikely to be worthwhile unless there is at least a lorry load of about 20 tonnes available in the case of hardwoods, or say a valuable crop of good quality Douglas fir. Moving contractors and machinery to harvest small areas can be costly and difficult to arrange. A harvesting company might fit small jobs in with their programme by arrangement, and it is sometimes possible to find cutters who will tackle small jobs at weekends. (Safety is an important consideration, so make sure that those involved have been adequately trained – see Chapter 7.)

Table 4.4 indicates the approximate volumes of trees of varying dbh. This volume is roughly equivalent to the weight of wood in tonnes when the tree is felled – 10 tonnes of timber will be produced by three to four mature oak trees, eight to ten mature conifers and anything from 20 to over 100 pole-size thinnings. In the case of the mature oak only about one-third of the total volume of a tree is likely to be good quality timber, the remainder being chockwood (mining timber) and firewood.

The yield of timber from a forest is usually measured as cubic metres per hectare per year over the rotation length and is described as the yield class. For example, a stand of Yield Class 14 Douglas fir will produce an average of 14

What will it yield?

Table 4.4 Estimate of tree volume from dbh*

| dbh (cm) | Estimated volume (over bark) (m³) | |
	Conifers	Broad-leaves
5	0.01	0.01
10	0.04	0.04
15	0.1	0.1
20	0.25	0.25
25	0.45	0.4
30	0.7	0.6
35	1.0	0.9
40	1.5	1.2
45	2.0	1.5
50	2.5	1.9
60	3.6	2.6
70	4.6	3.3
80	–	4.2
100	–	6.0

(Source: MAFF, 1986)

* Figures are approximate: differences in tree shape may cause up to 50% variation from that shown. Volume of branchwood is *not* included; it typically represents an additional 20% in mature broad-leaves and mature open-grown conifers, and up to 50% in mature heavy-crowned open-grown broad-leaves and standards.

cubic metres per hectare per year for a rotation of 50 years. This yield includes thinnings and final volume at felling. Forestry Commission Yield Tables indicate the volume which can be expected for different tree species under normal growing conditions. They need to be treated with caution and results can be misleading. Yield control is an important subject in forestry, and training and advice are needed.

The length of the woodland cycle or rotation depends on the tree species involved and the intended market for the timber. The normal rotation span, the time taken for the trees to reach maturity, is 40–150 or more years, depending on circumstances. If you can retain some trees in the stand past their normal rotation age, landscape and wildlife conservation will benefit. However, over-mature trees are prone to disease and dieback and can become dangerous to users of the wood, and the commercial value of any such trees will probably be lost.

An overview of the features to assess for timber production is given in Table 4.5. If you intend to sell trees for firewood, rather than timber, you will still need to answer most of the questions raised in this section: what stage of growth is it at, what will it yield, and how good is the access? The tree species involved and their freedom from defects will be less important although hardwoods usually fetch a higher price for firewood than softwoods. It is not unusual for the costs involved in cutting and extracting firewood to exceed the income.

Wood-pasture

Woodlands are sometimes used to shelter stock in winter and for grazing. The light crown and deciduous nature of larch provide good conditions for grass to grow after the early thinnings have reduced the canopy. This was practised fairly extensively on the Atholl Estate in Perthshire chiefly for sheep grazing, and is still seen in places today. In England, forests were used more extensively in the past to produce feed for stock, mainly deer, by cutting the lower branches or pollarding. In these examples the commercial benefit from the forest was increased, the penalty being the decline of forest litter and forest plants and the prevention of natural regeneration. Today, Atholl Estate's undergrazed larch is zoned, grazing being excluded in an approximately 20 year rotation to allow natural regeneration of larch, birch, rowan and other tree species together with their associated flora and fauna.

In agroforestry, as the trees grow the timber value increases while the grazing revenue declines as the ground is progressively shaded. The aim is to produce high quality timber and **pruning** is essential to produce a saleable **butt** log. Long-standing examples of agroforestry include shared fruit production with grazing, poplar-growing with both grazing and grain production, and Christmas tree production with rotational grazing. The size of animal and the soil type will determine what it is possible to crop. The height of a cow will allow it to reach and damage many crops and its weight will make it unsuitable for wet heavy soil conditions where compaction and road damage may occur. Sheep are generally kinder to roads, culverts and drains, and ideal for grazing Christmas tree plantations if they are moved frequently to give them fresh suitable grasses and keep their attention away from the tree crop.

Whatever the wood-pasture system, old or new, an assessment involves the following points:

▶ tree species;

▶ development stage;

Table 4.5 Assessing woodland for commercial timber production (these features need to be assessed for each compartment)

Question	Feature	Measured by or observed from
1 What is the crop?	Species	Visual characteristics. Many stands are of mixed species; note only main ones
	Area	Plan of wood. Simple ground survey
	Origin (of woodland)	Number of stems per 'tree' and habit. Pure or mixed species. Even-aged/uneven-aged stands. Presence of archaeological features – ditches, ancient hedges, banks. Evidence of straight lines of trees indicates planting
2 What stage of growth is it at?	Age	Woodland records/planting date. Can be roughly estimated from tree size (diameter). An accurate measure can be obtained from felling a tree and counting the annual rings. Some stands will have trees of quite different ages, e.g. coppice with standards. Note age of each major component (see Table 4.1)
	Tree size	By dbh. Usually worth measuring all trees over 30 cm dbh, but only a representative sample of smaller ones (see Tables 4.1 and 4.4)
3 How good is its quality?	Health and growth	Signs of poor growth are short new shoots at branch tips, sparse foliage, severe defoliation, crown die-back, and fungi, holes or fluid on the bark. If a tree is felled to assess age, examine width of recent annual rings; if becoming close together, growth has been slowing and health may be poor
	Stand quality	Straight, defect-free tree trunks are best. Quality declines with increasing incidence of forking, twisting, fluting, curvature and branching on lower stem (bottom 6 m)
4 What will it yield (and when)?	Total quantity of timber	From adding together individual tree sizes calculated from diameters (see Table 4.4)
	Stocking	Count number of usable trees (>7 cm dbh) per unit area and calculate number per hectare or estimate average distance (spacing) between trees. Whether a stand is over- or understocked can be judged from the broad relationship with age or mean diameter (see Tables 4.3 and 4.4)

(Source: after MAFF, 1986)

- ▶ timber quality;
- ▶ whether there is or should be natural regeneration of the species;
- ▶ whether the present tree stocking and natural regeneration could form a crop;
- ▶ whether a tree crop is required;
- ▶ whether grazing is an acceptable option;
- ▶ the percentage tree cover and hence the nature of the sward and its value for grazing animals (trees usually have little effect on the sward until there is more than 50% tree cover);
- ▶ whether the tree crop is safe from grazing animals;
- ▶ whether there are fences and whether they are in good condition.

Game management

Woodlands can be developed to provide a habitat for game, usually pheasants and/or deer. The rent income per hectare for shooting can be sizeable but returns vary from region to region and are proportional to the costs of establishing and/or maintaining the operation. Woodland managed for game should be sited well away from houses and hence people and their cats and dogs for the obvious safety reasons and also to minimise disturbance.

Pheasants

The main factors determining the value of woodland for game shooting are the size, shape, siting and holding capacity for pheasants. Woods, copses, spinneys and belts of 1 to 5 hectares are generally the most valuable for game and shooting. This is partly because pheasants prefer woodland edges, and provided the wood is wide enough to keep the birds warm, the greater the amount of woodland edge the better. Another reason for preferring small woods and shelter belts is that a few individual guns or beaters can flush out the birds with the least effort. Where new shoots are being planned, the site should be chosen to encourage birds to fly high using natural contours, and with new plantings to fit into the landscape.

The suitability of woodland for holding pheasants in late autumn depends on the shrub cover and marginal shelter. An open, cold and windy woodland floor is equally inhospitable under broad-leaves or under conifers. The most suitable woodland for pheasants in descending order is:

1 managed traditional coppice;
2 young mixed conifer/broad-leaved woodland;
3 broad-leaved woodland with an open canopy and a shrub layer;
4 mature broad-leaved woodland with a closed canopy and bare floor;
5 mature coniferous woodland with a closed canopy and bare floor.

For example, six or seven woodland blocks of mixed age and species, from 2–15 hectares, with some rough ground or marsh and surrounded by 15–200 hectares of farmland (chiefly grass, with some roots and grain) could support a well-organised, expensive shooting syndicate, especially if the surrounding land is also keepered and shot over. Alternatively, two or three small woods of 1–3 hectares on a small mixed farm with odd corners of rough ground, some wet areas and hedges could make a very nice rough shoot without artificially rearing the birds if they were lightly fed in winter. Food is usually the limiting factor and heavy feeding can hold birds, even on poor ground, but it is expensive.

Six species of deer occur in Great Britain. The red and roe deer are native, the fallow deer was an early introduction by the Romans and Normans, and the sika, muntjac and Chinese water deer were released or escaped into the wild within the last century or so. Only the last one is still very localised in distribution.

Revenue can be earned from selling venison especially from red deer, and from sporting fees. Small landowners are unlikely to have large enough areas of woodland to make commercial deer stalking viable unless they form a syndicate with neighbouring owners. Where the woodland area is small, part-time amateur stalkers can help to limit damage and produce a crop of venison, provided they are adequately covered for third party insurance and are experienced, safe and reliable.

Unlike some other sporting animals, deer can cause damage in woodland, farms and gardens. Deer management needs to strike a balance between the benefits to be obtained from hunting and the need to control the numbers. Culling deer will not entirely prevent damage to trees and, where a crop is being planted or naturally regenerated, deer fencing or individual tree protection may be needed.

If birch, willow, ash and low-growing shrubs have been encouraged along the woodland edge, pressure on the commercial crop may be relieved. Gaps, clearings, unplanted areas, natural open avenues beside streams, wider rides and forest roads with unplanted verges all give the deer access to areas where they can enjoy the warmth of direct sunlight and feed on the vegetation along the forest edge. These are also useful areas for observing, counting and culling deer. Depending on the lie of the land and access, such areas can be stalked either on foot or from a high seat (if thoughtfully sited and well-built, these can have a long, useful life, and are an important aid to deer culling).

Recreation

Woodlands can absorb large numbers of people in a small area without seeming crowded. Broad-leaved or mixed woodlands present a changing picture through the seasons, and their structural diversity, which is useful for wildlife, is also important for recreational use. Coniferous forests, even when managed to maximise commercial returns, can be used for recreation, for picnicking and walking for instance, if suitably managed. Farm woodlands can be ideally placed for some forms of recreation, offering the variety of open farmland and enclosed woodland close together. Woodland managed for recreation can create business opportunities (particularly in tourist areas, near centres of population and on the urban fringe) or can be a highly valued free recreational resource for the local community.

Each woodland is different, and the potential for access depends on its age, other uses, silvicultural operations and the views of the owner. Recreation potential is generally greater in existing than in newly planted woodland. Mature woodland, or woodland with a diverse structure including trees of different ages, open areas and rides, and additional features such as water, is particularly suited to recreation. Most people visiting woodlands appreciate the sense of freedom, but at the same time they like to know where they can walk and what they can do and they generally prefer to walk along forest roads, rides and tracks. A few are less responsible but experience has shown that physical and legal exclusion are rarely effective. Indeed, the presence of larger numbers of responsible people may act as a deterrent to vandalism.

There may already be public access to the woodland by footpaths, bridleways or byways. The local highway authority (usually the county council) holds the definitive map of statutory rights of way for its area and this is available for public inspection. Owners have a duty not to obstruct public rights of way (see the *Legislation and Regulations* booklet), and plans for planting and subsequent woodland management must ensure that they are kept clear.

Facilities

If recreation involving woodland is to be a means of supplementing income, facilities such as car parks, picnic places, toilets and viewpoints may be necessary. Woodland roads and tracks can be used for walking, riding or cycling if adequately surfaced. Opportunities may exist to use the woodland as part of an existing recreational or tourist business, as part of a farm trail or as a place for camping or caravaning. Some specialist activities can be attracted to woodlands – horse-riding circuits, off-road motor-cycling, survival/war games, orienteering and clay pigeon shooting for example. Where such activities are planned, an attempt should be made to zone areas according to different degrees of usage. This is especially important in woods which are in some form of public ownership and receive many visitors or where damage to the wildlife interests may result.

Liability

Woodland owners in places frequented by the public are responsible for assessing tree health and, as far as possible, removing dangerous trees and branches. Deciding whether a tree is dangerous can be difficult and is best done by a professional arboriculturist. However, as a general guide, be particularly wary of trees which are over-mature or show signs of fungal attack. Branches which overhang paths are a particular hazard, especially for riders.

4.2 *Integrating conservation and business assessments*

If the conservation and business aspects of woodland management are considered in isolation, they tend to become increasingly incompatible. On the other hand, if they are closely integrated, many synergies (or beneficial interactions) can be developed.

For example, valuable hardwood timber can be harvested from broad-leaved ancient, semi-natural high forest and, providing great care is taken during timber extraction, little damage will be done to the wildlife value of the wood. At the other extreme, there is much that can be done to enhance the conservation value of coniferous plantations without damaging their commercial value. Thus, the interactions between timber production and wildlife conservation result in only moderate, localised conflict and also provide moderate localised synergy (see Table 4.6).

Table 4.6 was drawn up from a generalised and optimistic perspective – there are many instances where commercial timber production does result in considerable conflict with game, recreation, wildlife and landscape with little or no synergy, but this need not be the case.

Table 4.6 Interactions between business and conservation aspects of woodland

← *CONFLICTS* →

↑ SYNERGIES ↓

	Timber production	Other wood products	Game	Recreation	Landscape	Wildlife
Timber production		○	○○	○○	○○	○○
Other wood products	★★★		○	○	○	○
Game	★★	★★★		○	○	○○
Recreation	★★	★★★	★		○	○○
Landscape	★★★	★★★	★★★	★★★		○
Wildlife	★★	★★★	★★	★★	★★★	

★ = little synergy
★★ = moderate, localised synergy
★★★ = considerable synergy
○ = little conflict
○○ = moderate, localised conflict
○○○ = considerable conflict

For specific land areas, you could draw up a series of tables like Table 4.6, one for each timber stand, indicating the present status of the interactions between conservation and commercial aspects and also drawing attention to the areas where improvement is possible. The aim should be to minimise the level of conflict and maximise the synergy. The generalised version in Table 4.6 also shows how woodland managed for other wood products, such as firewood or small wood from coppiced stands, results in less conflict than timber production and more synergy with conservation uses of woodland. Management for game, like wildlife, is moderately compatible with timber production and even more compatible with management for other wood products. It also has considerable benefits for the landscape. However, where woodland is managed intensively for game, as with any other intensive system of management, there can be at least moderate, localised conflict with wildlife. In Chapter 5 a variety of ways in which such conflicts can be minimised and synergy maximised are suggested.

If you do the initial assessment of any land area so as to integrate business and conservation aspects in a constructive way, it will help to achieve an *optimum* management plan with a higher overall benefit than if you concentrate on one or other aspect in isolation.

You will need to consider how landscape and wildlife aspects interact and how both interact with the business assessment. If you have more than one stand of trees, you will need to think about how they interact.

Maintain, enhance, create

If an area of woodland has a very high wildlife and landscape value, you will want to maintain it and make sure it does not decline. The best option for such areas may be to leave them to develop naturally for many years, but most woodland will need some management from time to time to maintain its conservation value.

Woodland that has a high conservation value and is not being managed for timber can often be left undisturbed for 50 years or more – there is no urgent need to act and some woods can be left alone altogether.

Woodland that is only moderately good from a conservation point of view can probably be upgraded and areas with no conservation interest can be greatly improved. These requirements will inevitably place a few constraints on the commercial management of the woodland, but they will also open up a range of new opportunities.

Landscape and wildlife interactions

Landscape and wildlife conservation usually reinforce one another in woodland management. Thus, the presence of a range of tree species, a broken canopy, a rich understorey structure and an uneven and diverse woodland edge will all count as positive contributions to both landscape and wildlife. The distinction is that, where landscape is concerned, more attention is paid to the visual aspects – how shapes and colours interact with one another and with the non-wooded areas of the landscape – than to the species involved. For wildlife conservation, on the other hand, the presence of native, rather than non-native species and the length of time the woodland has been in existence will usually be much more important than their actual lay-out on the ground. However, few people will be interested exclusively in one or the other aspect; most would prefer to see woodland with a high rating on both criteria. In Table 4.6 there is therefore little conflict between wildlife and landscape and considerable synergy.

64

Conservation and business interactions

One way to make conservation and business interactions explicit is to think about how various woodland management activities have, in the past, affected wildlife and landscape value positively or negatively, and vice versa; for example as follows.

▶ Has public access prevented the use of woodland for game and/or damaged its wildlife interest?

▶ Has extensive use of weedkillers around young trees affected the range of plants in the herb and ground layers of the wood?

▶ Have some glades been left unplanted in commercial woodland and/or have wide rides been cleared?

▶ Has over-grazing in the woodland damaged the diversity of the understorey and/or the quality of the timber?

▶ Has the extraction of timber in the past damaged the conservation value of rides and glades?

▶ Has natural regeneration been allowed at the woodland edge?

▶ Have non-native species been used for game cover?

▶ Is the tree canopy too dense to allow the growth of a woodland understorey?

▶ Have some fallen trees been allowed to decay naturally rather than being cleared away?

▶ In coniferous plantations, have the planted areas been kept well back from streams, rivers, lakes or lochs?

Woodland in its context

An integrated assessment should view the woodland areas in the context of the land holding as a whole, as described in the foundation book. The woodland areas should also be considered in relation to one another – if they are separated by land used for other purposes, are they close enough to interact with one another and are they connected by boundary habitats such as hedgerows or ditches? If you are dealing with large areas of forested land, how do various compartments relate to one another and what is the situation at the boundaries of the woodland?

This book does not deal with management planning as such, but some mention has to be made of the land manager's objectives and the constraints under which she or he is operating. For example, in the case studies without this information it is impossible to make the transition from the integrated assessment to a consideration of the various options open to the manager to resolve the problems and take up the opportunities identified.

The way woodland has been managed in the past, and hence the nature of the integrated assessment, will depend on what the objectives and constraints have been. The assessment may show up a need to make some changes in the objectives or may suggest opportunities to remove some constraints; alternatively, a change in objectives, for example from straightforwardly commercial to mixed commercial and conservation, may have been the stimulus to make the assessment in the first place.

4.3   Making your own integrated assessment

Make an integrated assessment of the woodland in your own study area, following the case study examples in the next section. It should include:

▶   a business assessment summary for the woodland area, for example as shown in Table 4.7, for each relevant compartment or stand, to take account of timber and/or fuel wood production, wood-pasture, game and recreation, as appropriate;

▶   where appropriate, a map showing the relationship of woodland to other land uses, as shown in Figure 4.2;

▶   an indication of the land manager's objectives and relevant constraints;

▶   a description of the perceived problems and opportunities and also past management successes, making sure that areas of present or potential conflict between commercial aspects and conservation, and also areas of synergy, are covered.

4.4   Integrated assessment of case study areas

Killiehangie Hill, Atholl Estate

Table 4.7 is a summary of the business assessment for this area of the estate. The main tree species are Norway and Sitka spruce and hybrid larch. The larch gives a falsely inflated impression of its numbers as it has been planted mainly on ridges and knolls and on the top of the hills.

This is an area of high quality, traditional commercial forest. In the previous two forestry rotations, the entire hillside was cut in one operation and sawmills were specially installed to deal with the crop. The present crop was previously part of a Dedication Scheme but was pulled out of it 3 years ago. It is now being put into a Woodland Grant Scheme.

The owner's general objectives and attitude were described in Section 1.5. Among the constraints on management could be included the increasing demand for public access and planning requirements resulting from increased public awareness of land use issues. However, financial constraints caused by changes in UK policy and grant schemes, and by changes in the exchange rates and policies of major timber-producing countries like Scandinavia and Canada, have been much more important. In the past these have priced home-grown timber off the market, to a point where round timber could not be sold and replanting virtually ceased for years at a time. Changes in the tax arrangements have had similar effects. In 1989 the estate's tree nurseries were unable to sell plants because of a cut-back in planting after changes to the tax arrangements for forestry in the 1989 budget.

The Atholl woodland's experience shows that reasonable trading conditions will result in a 'relaxed' approach to non-commercial aspects, while stop–go

Table 4.7   Woodland business assessment for Killiehangie Hill

(Separate assessment to be done for each compartment or stand)

Stand name/location   Killiehangie Hill, middle slope zone   Date 4/5/89

Sketch map

see Figure 4.1

Soil type(s)/grade(s)   Schistose in origin, deposited rubble on lower slopes

Timber and firewood production

Commercially useful species   30% hybrid larch, 40% Norway spruce, 10% Douglas Fir,
Area Approx. 40 ha   15% Sitka Spruce, 5% Birch and mixed broad-leaves
Origin Planted forest, pre-1600
Age Plantation at thinning stage
Tree size Average 18 cm dbh
Health and growth{ Norway spruce severely damaged by red deer, other species in good health and
Stand quality   ʃ form, although larch windswept in parts
Total quantity of timber 40 ha × 160 m³ = 6400 m³
Stocking density 800/ha
Accessibility Very poor
Legislation/designations: TPO, felling licence, SSSI, WGS

Wood-pasture

Percentage tree cover
Sward quality   Area has no potential for wood-pasture. Very expensive to fence
Level of tree protection

Game

Woodland type: coppice, mixed, broad-leaved (coniferous)   Not good for pheasants due to
Woodland structure: open canopy, (closed canopy), shrub layer, (bare floor) even-aged structure. Deer are
                                                                a pest but not managed for game.

Recreation

Access (number and location of footpaths, etc.)
Facilities
Liabilities

67

policies and difficult trading conditions result in disruption to the programme and a harder look being taken at non-quantifiable benefits.

The management plan

The management system for the Atholl woodlands, regardless of the woodland scheme in operation at the time, consists of:

▶ maps breaking down woodlands into compartments, ideally with boundaries consisting of recognisable features such as rides, streams or walls, and showing compartment numbers and their area (see Figure 4.1);

▶ a description of the area – topography, rainfall, elevation, soils, vegetation;

▶ a statement of the management objectives;

▶ a 5-year plan showing planting, felling, thinning and other prescriptions;

▶ the manager maintaining more regular contact with the owner by producing a yearly programme of work showing the felling, planting, thinning and maintenance programmes;

▶ annual estimates of income and expenditure, broken down between woodlands, sawmills and nursery, and for the various forest operations;

▶ monthly management accounts showing true costs, invoiced sales and bank statements to show the cash flow position and to monitor income and expenditure.

Every compartment is checked formally at least once in 5 years even though no work is required. The manager continually checks the health of trees and monitors the rabbit and deer populations.

The main stimulus for this assessment was the large-scale encroachment of deer from the open hill land. The hill forms part of the western boundary of the Atholl Estate, and the boundary wall has not been deer-proof for decades. A few over-wintering stags began to use the hill and their numbers have increased considerably over the last 3 or 4 years (deer-fencing operations in nearby areas might have played a part in this). Damage to Norway spruce in the early thinning stage started about 3–4 years ago, reaching severe proportions when thinning was actually under way a year ago, brashed areas suffering most.

It would be uneconomic to leave the most severely damaged areas of Norway spruce in their present condition and the manager is considering premature felling, which will require a Forestry Commission felling licence. This will also provide an opportunity to alter the boundaries and shape of the compartment, and the species mix at replanting, so as to increase the structural and species diversity of the whole area and not just the broad-leaved areas.

Small woods in Sussex

This mixed farm occupies 408 hectares on six different soil types. Some 230 hectares are owner-occupied, the remainder, including all the downland, is rented. The main farm enterprises are as follows (see also Figure 4.2).

Arable

▶ Just over 110 hectares of cereal crops, mainly winter wheat

▶ Nearly 40 hectares of break crops, mostly oilseed rape

▶ About 60 hectares of temporary grassland

▶ 84 hectares of permanent grassland

▶ 60 hectares of rough grazing

Livestock

▶ A dairy herd of 216 milking cows fed on summer pasture and winter silage

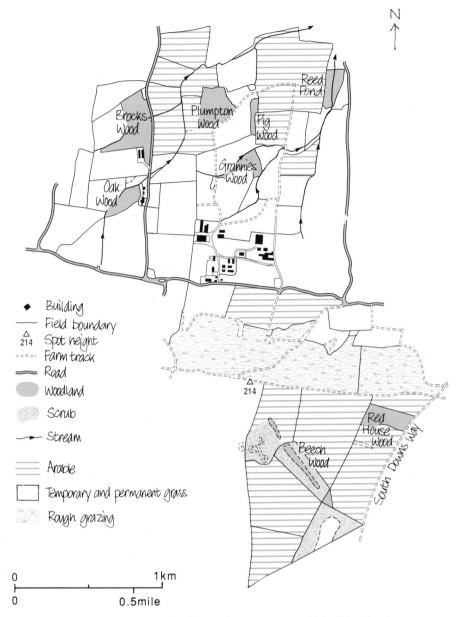

N
↑

Key:
- ◆ Building
- — Field boundary
- △ 214 Spot height
- --- Farm track
- ══ Road
- Woodland
- Scrub
- → Stream
- Arable
- Temporary and permanent grass
- Rough grazing

```
0                    1km
├────┬────┬────┬────┤
0          0.5mile
```

Figure 4.2   Land use on the case study farm

▶ Rearing of replacement heifers and running a small bull beef unit

▶ A flock of 400 cross-bred breeding ewes rearing finished lambs

The primary objective of the farm is to operate as a commercial unit with some *Objectives* investment income available at the end of the year. The secondary objective is to act as an educational resource for farmers and the public alike. Important conservation sites have been identified in various surveys (see Section 3.6) and through advice from the local Farming and Wildlife Advisory Group; these are now included in the farm manager's plans.

Over the last 30–40 years farm policy towards the woodland has largely been *Woodland* one of non-intervention. During the last 3–4 years, however, some of the woods have been cleared back to their original boundaries (in some cases the woods had been allowed to encroach 20 metres into the field). At the same

Table 4.8 Woodland business assessment for case study farm

(Separate assessment to be done for each compartment or stand)

Stand name/location *Plumpton Wood*   Date *May 1989*

Sketch map

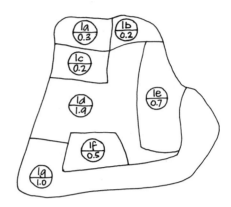

Soil type(s)/grade(s) *Gault clay*

Timber and firewood production

Commercially useful species *Oak standards / hazel coppice / regenerating ash*
Area *4.88 ha*
Origin *Semi-natural but management history as coppice-with-standards*
Age *Pre-1600*
Tree size *Oaks 25-70 cm dbh. Mature coppice*
Health and growth *Variable but mostly poor.*
Stand quality *Low quality. Better trees removed 40-50 years ago. Some good young ash*
Total quantity of timber *350-400 m³ of timber and underwood.*
Stocking density *25/ha*
Accessibility *Good. Tracks to wood, rides within*
Legislation/designations: TPO, felling licence, SSSI, (WGS)

Wood-pasture

Percentage tree cover
Sward quality   *N/A*
Level of tree protection

Game

Woodland type: coppice, mixed, broad-leaved, coniferous   *N/A*
Woodland structure: open canopy, closed canopy, shrub layer, bare floor

Recreation

Access (number and location of footpaths, etc.) *None, but some horses and walkers allowed.*
Facilities *None*
Liabilities *Potential problem from bee hives in wood.*

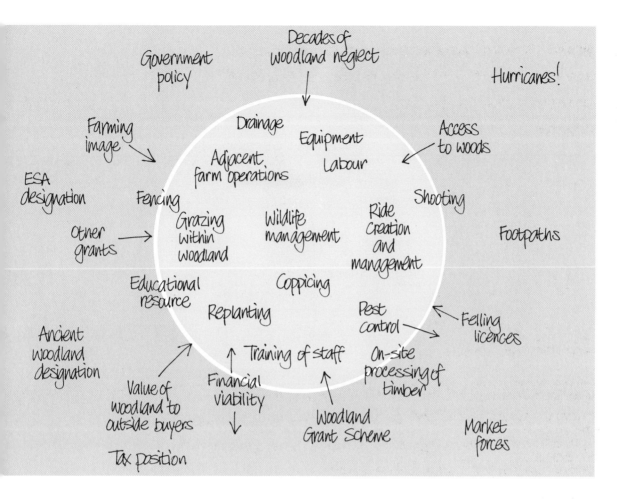

Figure 4.3 *Factors affecting the woodland on the case study farm. (Factors inside the circle are seen as under the control of the land manager. Those outside it are not. The arrows indicate those factors that seem to be changing, moving out of or into control)*

time boundary ditches were cleared and fences put up. Although aimed at improving the land's farming potential this operation has also uncovered some interesting old boundary banks and has created a dense edge to the wood whilst reducing shade onto the adjacent crop.

In 1988 it was decided that a more positive approach should be made to the management of the woods. This was prompted by the increased interest in woodlands in general, the availability of Forestry Commission grant aid and by the impact of the hurricane of October 1987. A consultant was employed to assess the woods (Table 4.8), to evaluate, in conjunction with the farm manager, the factors affecting the woodland on the farm (Figure 4.3) and to produce an objectives hierarchy for an integrated assessment (Figure 4.4, and Section 5.5 of the foundation book). Eventually, the same consultant drew up a Woodland Grant Scheme for all of the farm's woodlands (see Section 6.6).

Problems and opportunities

CASE STUDY 4

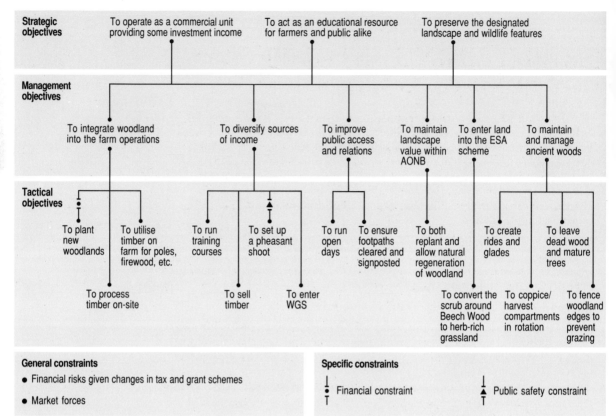

Strategic objectives

To operate as a commercial unit providing some investment income

To act as an educational resource for farmers and public alike

To preserve the designated landscape and wildlife features

Management objectives

To integrate woodland into the farm operations

To diversify sources of income

To improve public access and relations

To maintain landscape value within AONB

To enter land into the ESA scheme

To maintain and manage ancient woods

Tactical objectives

To plant new woodlands

To utilise timber on farm for poles, firewood, etc.

To run training courses

To set up a pheasant shoot

To run open days

To ensure footpaths cleared and signposted

To both replant and allow natural regeneration of woodland

To create rides and glades

To leave dead wood and mature trees

To process timber on-site

To sell timber

To enter WGS

To convert the scrub around Beech Wood to herb-rich grassland

To coppice/harvest compartments in rotation

To fence woodland edges to prevent grazing

General constraints

- Financial risks given changes in tax and grant schemes
- Market forces

Specific constraints

Financial constraint

Public safety constraint

Figure 4.4 Objectives hierarchy for the woodland on the case study farm (see Section 5.5 of the foundation book for further explanation of this technique)

72

Chapter 5

MAINTAINING AND IMPROVING EXISTING WOODLAND

The first stage of a full management planning exercise involves finding out 'where you are now' by making an integrated assessment of your local area, as described in Chapters 2, 3 and 4. This leads on to a consideration of 'where you would like to be' – exploring the strategic, management and tactical objectives for the land area as a whole – as described in the foundation book and as illustrated briefly in the case studies at the end of Chapter 4. This chapter concerns the next stage – the range of options available to put your objectives into practice.

When conservation is one of the objectives of woodland management, the appropriate options will depend on the wood's present landscape and wildlife quality, and how they interact with the business aspects, i.e. the information collected for your integrated assessment.

Appropriate management options fall into three categories:

1   *maintaining* woodland in its present form because it is a valued landscape feature or because it is a rare ecological type or contains rare plants and/or animals or because it is classified as ancient and therefore of high ecological value;
2   *improving* woodland of moderate or poor conservation value, by changing its visual appearance or by increasing the overall ecological diversity and/or encouraging particular wildlife species;
3   *creating* new woodland designed to blend in with the landscape and/or to support and encourage a wide diversity of wildlife and/or particular wildlife species.

This chapter concentrates on the first two categories, looking at conservation within existing woodlands, whether it be a small broad-leaved copse or a coniferous forest, and whether the objectives of the woodland management are to provide timber, game, recreation, landscape value or wildlife habitat. In each case you have to work with what is already there and, because woodland is a slow-growing habitat, you need to think on a long-term time scale. In the next chapter, which looks at the creation of *new* woodlands, many of the considerations are the same as for existing woodland, but the ability to design for specific objectives is greater on a 'green field' site.

5.1   *Maintaining high value woodland*

If a piece of woodland is assessed as being of high conservation value (see Chapters 2 and 3) the most appropriate action may be not to intervene but to allow nature to take its course. Alternatively, you may need to continue the traditional, long-term management practices that have been responsible for the present high quality of the woodland, or to reinstate such traditional management where it has fallen into disuse.

Non-intervention

If woodland is already of high conservation value, with no signs of deterioration, the best long-term option for its management is to leave it alone, re-surveying it every 5 years or so to monitor its quality. Because woodland is a climax community it can under natural conditions remain as woodland over periods of hundreds of years. Even severe windthrow is a natural phenomenon, and affected woods will usually regenerate naturally, provided grazing animals (including rabbits) are not present in large numbers. Quality may gradually deteriorate if, for example, there is no natural regeneration because of grazing pressure or because of a very dense, closed canopy, or if invasive broad-leaved species such as sycamore are becoming dominant or if valuable open space in the wood is being lost by scrubbing up.

Traditional management practices

Where ancient or high woodland has recently been or is being managed, the continuation of these practices will help to ensure that the conservation value is retained. If management practices are confined to small compartments and staggered in time they will create least disturbance. When ancient woodland is clear felled in small blocks there need not be any loss of plant species in the long term provided it is replanted or allowed to regenerate with the same native species of local **provenance**. There will be a temporary loss of animals, particularly invertebrates that feed on the trees and birds that feed on the invertebrates. These animals will be able to recolonise the woodland if there is another suitable stand at the right stage of growth nearby. That is why felling and replanting small compartments at a time allows the greatest diversity of wildlife to thrive.

Coppice restoration

An important traditional woodland management system is coppicing. Coppice woodland is found in most areas from the Scottish borders to the south of England, the proportion increasing to the south. It is most common in Kent, Surrey and Sussex where it forms over 1% of the total land area. Coppice crops are usually worked in small **coupes**, so that even small woodlands contain several age classes. This provides structural diversity, an increased extent of 'edge' effect, and therefore a variety of habitats supporting a wide range of wildlife species.

The relatively short rotation means that the period of closed canopy is short, allowing seeds of herbaceous and other ground flora to survive and to take advantage of the influx of light after the next felling. Many traditional woodland flowers are at their best 2 to 3 years after coppicing, giving spectacular displays, especially in the spring. Though the quantity of herbaceous plants may be greatest in the years immediately after coppicing the total number of species may continue to increase up until about the fifth year.

Many coppices have been worked for hundreds of years and this continual fairly rapid cycling of the ecosystem between cleared woodland and closed canopy has encouraged the survival of many woodland species not readily able to colonise new woodland such as oxlip. Regular coppicing also enables individual trees to survive for a very long time without ever becoming mature. Some stools are over a thousand years old. However, once a tree has been allowed to reach maturity, it is less likely to be able to regenerate as coppice after being cut down. The stump will often die.

Where a coppiced wood has been singled and managed as high forest ('stored coppice') the associated plant and animal species will probably have seriously declined. The option of bringing stored coppice back into coppice management to improve the wildlife diversity may not be straightforward in practice. Unless the area has been coppiced within the previous 30–40 years and there is a potential source of both plants and animals (including invertebrates) for colonisation, the species diversity may not improve. In the absence of colonising species, a return to coppice management can create the opportunity for an invasive species such as bramble to dominate the shrub layer of restored coppice, sometimes to the extent of affecting the regeneration of the coppiced trees.

As it is difficult to predict the outcome of reintroducing coppicing after a long period of neglect, you should experiment first with a small area. If the regenerating ground flora has few interesting species, you may be able to collect seed from a nearby source, provided you have the owner's permission, it is not an ancient woodland and the species concerned are not protected (see the *Legislation and Regulations* booklet.) If the trees have reached maturity, you may need to replant or wait for natural regeneration to restore the woodland, a much slower process than successful coppicing. Under circumstances like these, it is probably best to leave the wood as high forest, adopting some of the suggestions in Section 5.2 to improve its conservation value.

5.2   *Enhancing low value woodland*

Woodland that is of moderate or poor wildlife conservation value is unlikely to improve if left alone, so enhancement depends on some degree of management. Three major options for improvement should be considered:

1   undertaking management operations that impinge on the whole of the woodland and its associated flora and fauna;

2   concentrating on marginal parts of the woodland such as the woodland edge, glades, rides and ponds; or

3   managing the woodland to suit particular groups of plants or animals, e.g. bluebells, butterflies or birds.

Whole woodland management

If the woodland as a whole is being managed, some form of commercial timber production is usually envisaged. Timber production can involve anything from producing firewood and stakes for use on the farm to producing high quality timber for joinery and veneers (see Table 4.2).

This section outlines briefly the management operations in commercial woodland and indicates where and how they can be modified to give a greater benefit to wildlife habitats and the landscape.

The woodland management cycle

Much commercial woodland or forest is managed along similar lines to an agricultural crop, on rotations lasting anything from 15 to 150 years, with a clearly-defined cycle of management activities, as outlined in Box 4.1. However, even where the production of a viable timber crop is the first consideration, it is not necessary to forget the visual and conservation aspects.

This section shows how these and other management activities can be adapted or modified to increase the benefit, or reduce the hazard, to wildlife habitats and the landscape. Which options you should pursue for your own land will depend on the stage of development of the woodland and on your earlier assessment of its landscape and wildlife habitat value. Always bear in mind that you may not need to do anything at all for quite a number of years.

Because timber production is a long-term operation, faster-growing species are usually preferred by producers, to keep the rotation length to a minimum. This is often the reason for planting faster-growing non-native conifers. Although growth rates are slower on upland sites conifers can withstand the harsh, exposed conditions more successfully than broad-leaved species. Broad-leaved trees are unlikely to be commercially successful if grown at over 300 metres above sea level. However, they can be grown at quite high altitudes, especially if the site is protected to some extent from wind and frost. Conifers are often planted along with broad-leaved species to provide an earlier financial return, or to act as a **nurse crop** for the broad-leaved trees. The presence of conifers in the mixture will protect broad-leaved trees from frost and encourage them to grow more quickly.

Mixed species stands are often used for commercial timber production and, if managed sensitively, this can improve the landscape appearance and conservation value of the woodland (see also Chapter 6). The best commercial tree for a particular site can be planted on the greater part of the area, avoiding features such as rocky patches, gorges and wet places where commercial management is, in any case, of doubtful value. In coniferous woodland, variety can be introduced by choosing species to suit the naturally varying site conditions; for example, in the north, spruce in damp grassy areas, Scots pine on knolls, larch on intermediate slopes and Douglas fir in fertile, bouldered areas. Planting teams given these basic directions have a proven record of producing a visually attractive, commercially viable result. Alternatively, a proportion of broad-leaved species suitable to the site can be decided on in advance and planted out at random along with the commercial species.

Further diversity can be achieved by **beating up** with a change of species. Where large areas are being replanted, changes of species at the compartment boundary should be 'filtered' to avoid 'hard' edges. Small gaps in a stand caused by failures or by deer grazing can be left to add diversity, interest and valuable edge effect, and also to give opportunities for deer control.

On some commercial woodland sites, natural regeneration after felling or natural colonisation from adjoining woodland may be useful options for establishing woodland (see Table 5.1). Natural regeneration is a relatively cheap form of establishment but there can be increased costs around the thicket stage because of the need to thin any dense growth if suitable timber trees are to be grown. Some gaps may also need to be filled in. Natural regeneration does ensure that the trees are of local provenance, but the previous woodland composition may not have been the most suitable for wildlife or timber production and selective thinning may also be needed at the thicket stage.

Some species, such as sycamore, regenerate more quickly or successfully than others, so the tree composition of the new wood may be different from that of the previous wood. Another potential problem, particularly on clay soils, is that the water table rises significantly when the tree cover is removed which can hamper the establishment of some trees (even by planting), encourage the

Table 5.1 Comparison of natural regeneration with replanting

	Natural regeneration	Artificial regeneration (replanting)
As a timber management practice	Unreliable on some sites	Reliable
Source of seedlings	Arise 'freely' on site	Purchase from nursery
Stocking of new crop	May be patchy, varying from very dense to sparse, visually attractive	Uniform, but visually less attractive
Timing: felling previous crop	Determined by good seed years which complicates marketing and cash flow	Any time
year of establishment	Uncertain, depending on good seed years	Any year provided plants are available
season of planting	Not applicable	Late autumn or early spring
Genetics	Little opportunity for species change or crop improvement apart from ensuring good quality parent trees of local provenance	Opportunity to introduce new species or provenances, but often non-native
Tending	Shade from parent trees may reduce weed growth and lessen the need for tending, but early respacing of dense regeneration and infilling of gaps may both be needed	Immediate post-planting growth is usually slow and weed growth tends to be heavy, making regular weeding essential. Herbicide use reduces plant community
Other	Parent trees may give some protection from frost and ensure continuity of animal communities	Complete removal of previous crop leads to wetter ground conditions, especially on clay, and to serious reductions in the animal community

(Source: after Evans, 1984)

growth of tussock grasses and rushes and make the site prone to frost damage.

Seed years are intermittent and unpredictable for most species (every 5 or more years on average), so natural regeneration is a more uncertain option, although there is usually a reservoir of seed from previous years remaining in the soil.

Weeding stage

At this stage any natural regeneration of oak, birch or other species can be accepted into the stand, rather than being weeded out. Coppice shoots of ash and sycamore can also be incorporated, bearing in mind that sycamore, whilst being a good timber tree, is not as useful for wildlife conservation. Also its free-seeding habit and shade tolerance can make it very invasive.

At this stage, cleaning can be intensified to remove some deformed trees and also a few of the planted stock to free natural oak, birch, ash, wild cherry or other trees without greatly affecting the cash value of the crop and certainly enhancing its conservation, visual and sporting value. Removing **wolf** trees (large, coarse-branched trees) at the early stages lets light in for some lower vegetation without risking the wind damage which can occur if the crown is opened up too dramatically at later stages.

The key to all of this is moderation, avoiding any dramatic changes which will adversely affect the health and stability of the crop.

Help can continue to be given to some natural regeneration. In particular, the edges of the woods should not be neglected as in many cases a rich mixture of spruce, larch, oak, birch, ash, blackthorn and other species will emerge provided the cutters have been instructed to encourage them. The same will apply to the weeding team. Give woodland or forestry workers a clear list of priorities: for example, a good oak takes priority over a good larch; a good larch takes priority over a deformed oak; do not cut anything you don't recognise. This simple policy has been shown to improve diversity gradually without loss of revenue. But you must maintain the balance and seek help when in doubt.

For early thinning in even-aged large blocks of conifers, mechanical systems (**line thinnings**) have often been used, usually as an expedient in times of poor pulp and chipwood prices. The results, both visually and commercially, leave much to be desired. Thinning is usually and preferably **crown thinning** or **low thinning**. The first thinning will aim to remove, among other things, **whips** (tall, slender, suppressed trees) and wolf trees. Further thinning, probably on a 5-year cycle, will give growing space to the remaining crop by the removal of suppressed trees and the break up of the canopy by removing some dominant trees.

Unskilled marking for thinnings can result in a deterioration of the crop, loss of revenue and windblow. Take advice and if the job is too small to pay an expert, you might get less expensive advice from a retired forester or helpful guidance from your local forestry society.

At the felling stage the options for future management are decided. It might be that for a 100 hectare stand grown on a 100-year rotation, 1 hectare will be cut yearly. Much more likely under British conditions will be a preponderance of

And I thought – why stop at natural regeneration?

one age class, either young or mature stands, with the middle stages missing. Under these circumstances felling of mature wood could be deferred to enable the younger stands to 'catch up' so as to arrive at a sustained yield with all ages present. With this in mind the felling system should be aiming for a 'normal forest' where all stages of growth are present in a balanced state.

One area of woodland on the Atholl Estate has been managed in this way over many years. Sections of mature hybrid larch are harvested at intervals of 5–10 years, leaving a few of the better specimens standing to provide a source of seed for natural regeneration, and allowing a proportion of broad-leaved species to establish naturally at the same time. Eventually the area will become self-sustaining, providing a good income at regular intervals.

Clear felling and replanting is the usual method of regenerating both coniferous and broad-leaved high forest in Britain because it uses labour most efficiently and maximises the output from a stand. The size of the felling coupe will have a major influence on the extent to which there is landscape or habitat disruption. In broad-leaved woodland, coupes are typically small (between 1 and 3 hectares) and so have a small overall impact. In coniferous forest, coupes are usually much larger, but if the shape of the coupes is carefully designed and the scale of the landscape is large they can cause little visual intrusion (see Section 6.2). In commercial coniferous forest, the cleared area offers a new habitat opportunity to many wildlife species, rather than being a disadvantage.

Clear felling exposes surrounding trees to a greater chance of windthrow and, for thin-barked species such as beech and sycamore, **sun scorch**. Any large opening in the canopy will also encourage the development of **epicormic shoots** on exposed trunks, which reduces the timber quality of the tree, especially in the case of oaks for high quality veneers. Clear felling also opens up slopes to water erosion and encourages the silting up of lakes and streams.

Group felling is less environmentally disruptive than clear felling. It involves cutting down patches of less than 0.5 hectares in any one year and is well suited to smaller scale workings. Although there is less disturbance to the ecosystem group felling is usually more expensive than clear felling. A similar habitat effect is provided by a strip selection system, where only small strips are felled at one time, but this can have an unfortunate landscape impact.

It is also possible to underplant an existing crop with a second crop at some stage during the rotation. This produces a two-storey high forest for a few years until the overstorey is removed, usually before its shade impairs the growth of the new crop. The main example in Britain is where beech is introduced into young pole-stage stands of birch, mature pine or poorly growing ash or oak. Whatever the felling system, trees of wildlife or landscape interest, especially oak, some birch, holly, blackthorn and non-diseased dead trees, can be left in place to provide landscape interest and habitat diversity while the young trees are growing.

Whatever the felling system, the small branches and twigs (**lop and top**) from the harvested trees will be left on the site. This can be burnt or stacked around trees at felling time or mechanically pushed on to fires at the end of the job. In the winter months burning will cause little harm but avoid burning when birds are nesting. Indeed, the timing of management work to avoid the disturbance of wildlife is critical (see below).

It is not always necessary to clear lop and top. The breakdown of litter is an important component of a forest soil, enhancing the nutrient cycle. Lop and top can be cut down fairly tidily and in the subsequent planting the planters paid an increased rate to plant through it. This can help establishment, particularly on dry slopes, but weeding costs can be higher due to the difficulty of cutting weeds growing through brash. A further problem may be experienced in controlling rabbits – the dense cover gives them ideal shelter. However, pheasants are attracted to the ground cover for nesting and for shelter, so it makes good hiding and flushing ground.

The decision about what to do with lop and top will depend on the site and also on the owner's wishes. In practice it often helps to vary the approach to give a range of different results, so long as no serious harm or costs are incurred.

Coppicing

Coppicing was described in Section 5.1. The continued felling and regeneration of trees at intervals of less than 30 years is a useful way of providing a regular income from small **roundwood** and to encourage good wildlife and landscape features. It is a system which needs little maintenance after initial establishment. Beech, wild cherry and poplar only coppice well when young. The species most commonly coppiced are hazel, hornbeam, lime, oak and sweet chestnut.

There are many types of broad-leaved coppice regime (Table 5.2) but the majority are simple coppice. As with high forest, the smaller the coupe, the less the impact on landscape and wildlife, and having several compartments with staggered rotations provides both diversity and continuity of wildlife habitats.

The age at which coppice is felled depends on the size of roundwood required, the species and the site. Except for short rotation hazel, all normal coppice rotations are shorter than the rotation of maximum mean annual increment. There are several disadvantages to extending the rotation to maximise yield: the larger stumps may coppice less well; in mixed coppice the smaller coppice species, especially hazel, become suppressed; and the conservation value diminishes since fewer plants can survive the longer period of dormancy.

In principle coppice can be worked indefinitely, but site exhaustion and stool mortality may eventually lead to declining yields. The natural fertility of most lowland sites means that even intensive coppice for firewood can survive at least 30 years without requiring fertiliser. Up to 5% of stumps may die at each cutting, often due to careless harvesting practices. Some replacement is therefore likely to be necessary.

Whole woodland management summary

The following list summarises the options for the management of woodland as a whole.

▶ If possible, plant or allow natural regeneration of native tree and shrub species especially in ancient woods.

▶ Trees and shrubs should be of local provenance if possible as a greater variety of insects is associated with native trees and shrubs than with more recently introduced species – see Figure 3.3 of the foundation book.

▶ Except in the Highlands of Scotland or on high land or very exposed sites, broad-leaved trees are preferable to conifers as they form a dense canopy only for part of the year, encouraging a rich ground flora.

▶ Always retain or incorporate broad-leaved trees in conifer plantations.

▶ Thinning, especially crown thinning, at the thicket stage of a woodland cycle allows light to reach the woodland floor and reduces shading of the ground flora. Thinnings and prunings left on the woodland floor will help to protect the regenerating flora from grazing if deer or sheep are present.

Table 5.2 Coppice types and terminology

Type	Description	Comments
Simple coppice	Crop consists entirely of coppice all of which is worked on the same cycle (even-aged)	May consist of only one (pure) or several (mixed) species
Coppice with standards	Two-storey forest. Coppice (underwood) with scattering of trees (standards) being grown to timber size	Standards may be of seedling origin (maidens) or develop from a stump shoot left for the purpose (stored coppice). Standards retained for a period of 3–8 coppice cycles. Oak is much the commonest standard species
Stored coppice	Tree or stand of coppice origin as a result of growing coppice on beyond its normal rotation	Many woodlands, resembling high forest, are stored coppice owing to decline in coppice working this century
Short rotation coppice	Arbitrarily designated as coppice worked on a rotation of less than 10 years to produce stick-size material	Provides material for many rural crafts. Recent interest in production of biomass for energy

(Source: Evans, 1984)

▶ Leaving dead trees and pieces of large timber will provide a micro-habitat for fungi, wood-boring beetles and other animals.

▶ Extend the woodland cycle to allow some trees to become over-mature as these are particularly important for some **epiphytes** and as nesting sites for birds, as well as supporting an abundance of other plants and animals.

▶ Selectively fell the woodland in small coupes. This provides structural diversity and uneven-aged stands with all age classes present, allowing the survival of wildlife species adapted to particular stages of the woodland cycle, and providing reservoirs from which the wildlife species can colonise regenerating or replanted areas.

▶ Maintain coppice management where it is, or was, practised in the last 30 to 40 years.

▶ Avoid disturbing the soil surface too much when felling and extracting wood as this can reduce the seed bank of the native flora and damage the soil structure. However, some surface scuffing or **scarifying** can be beneficial to natural regeneration.

▶ Avoid working in the bird breeding season (March–July).

▶ Prevent grazing by domestic animals (except in recognised wood-pasture) to allow full re-establishment of the ground flora. However, a low level of grazing at particular times of the year may be beneficial.

▶ Always retain special features such as ponds, rides, glades, wet flushes, badger sets and rock outcrops or deformed or poorly growing trees because of their intrinsic landscape and wildlife conservation value.

► Accept opportunistic events such as windthrow or excessive deer grazing and retain as part of the woodland's structural diversity.

► Avoid using fertilisers in or near a wood and minimise herbicide use to spot treatments.

► Maintain rides and roads for access, extraction and wildlife interests (see below).

► Remove invasive, introduced shrub species such as rhododendron and snowberry as they suppress native shrubs and the ground flora. Whether or not you remove exotic tree species will depend on your other objectives. Sycamore generally reduces the conservation value of woodland but is a good timber tree.

Rides, glades and woodland margins

In commercial forest and other situations where there are no available resources or labour to manage the whole woodland for conservation, it is still possible to enhance the wildlife value by managing the margins – the edge, rides, roads, ponds, glades and other clearings. These areas add structural diversity and provide warm, sheltered and secluded open spaces. Since most animals feed along the edges of woods and rides, and predators follow them, the care of this habitat is rewarding and important. Visually, too, its care will produce diversity and interest. Broad-leaved shrubs and trees can be planted to provide some diversity at the edge of coniferous woodland, at irregular or random intervals and gaps can be left for colonisation by incoming seeds. Established margins may already contain shrubs and trees and you should try to prevent too much vigorous woody growth which leads to the margins becoming overgrown and heavily shaded. The shrubs that thrive in woodland margins grow quickly and may need to be cut back every 4 years on a rotational basis to allow smaller plants to grow and flower. Grass rides and verges should be cut, preferably in August, every 2 years, rather than annually, to ensure overwintering and feeding habitat, especially for invertebrates like butterflies. This can be done by cutting alternate sides or sections of the ride each year. Best results are achieved using a graded edge (see Figure 5.1). Rides are usually 6–8 metres wide. Forest roads are usually 9–12 metres wide, and

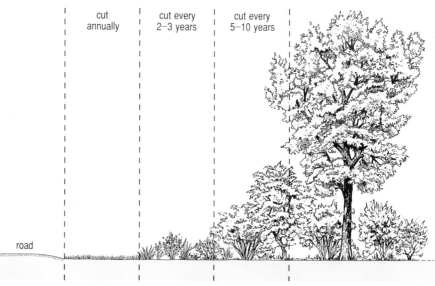

cut annually | cut every 2–3 years | cut every 5–10 years

road

Figure 5.1 Management of woodland edges to provide a graded structure

have a greater range of habitats than rides, including the crown of the road and the sloping verges and edge ditches rising up to banks into the wood, encouraging a greater variety of wildlife species.

It is better to keep a stable pattern of rides that are well maintained, because old rides generally have a greater species diversity than new rides. This applies to upland forests as much as to long-established lowland woods.

The management options are similar for rides, glades and margins. The margins can be thinned every 5 years, at the same time as the crop. This allows a fresh growth of native species, gives growing space to those already established and reduces competition from the main crop. Do not brash the perimeter trees as they keep the woods warm. The gaps left by the trees removed during the thinning operations will usually let in enough light to support the ground flora. Bare ground will enable seedlings to flourish and encourage natural regeneration of birch and other species. Oak will frequently flourish among coarse grasses, quite long distances from the parent tree, where acorns may have been carried by jays or dropped or buried by mice or grey squirrels as a food cache. The edges of rides, glades and margins can be cut artificially as noted above, but a continuous series of normal operations over the years will create a variety of conditions without any special effort. Bends in roads, rides and edges will give shelter from the wind from a variety of directions, and provide sunny spots. One possible option at the margins of woodland is to plant broad-leaved trees at a fairly wide spacing in a matrix of Norway spruce. The spruce can be harvested early as a Christmas tree cash crop, with easy access from the ride-side, leaving the broad-leaves as a permanent feature. (Make sure any spruces not cut for Christmas trees are removed at the pole stage.)

Where rides are narrower than is ideal, they can be widened at first thinning to produce a cash bonus. Any interesting natural regeneration of trees or shrubs can be left uncut.

Rides

For working purposes, wide rides are quicker drying and easier to maintain than narrow ones. Harvesting operations, especially timber extraction, can seriously damage the soil surface by cutting and rutting. Compaction is a more serious problem, especially on wet clay soils and trees will not grow on severely damaged areas. A badly rutted ride can be levelled by dragging a simple frame behind a tractor, causing little long-term damage to grass and plants. If used infrequently, grass rides can support vehicles approximately every 3 years, if the ground is dry when they are used.

In addition to timing operations where possible to avoid wet ground conditions, it is important to give careful instructions to any contractors to minimise the damage to rides during woodland management operations. For example, they can be confined to *agreed* routes by the contract of sale. However, they do have a job to do and if too tightly confined may not take on the job or may charge accordingly. Using the correct machine for the job can help to protect rides from damage – underpowered machines churn up the ground. It can be difficult to attract contractors for what they may see as a small fussy job.

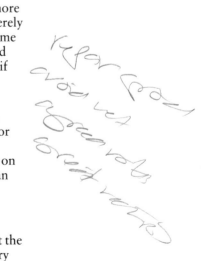

Common sense is required and also the confidence not to over-worry about the scarred appearance of some worked areas in the 'darkest' months of January and February. A little maintenance work can be done in March/April when the soil begins to dry out and by late May seeds will begin to germinate and hide the scars.

Table 5.3 Changes in conservation interest through the forestry cycle

	Stage in the woodland cycle:				
	Clear fell	Pre-thicket	Thicket	Mature	Over-mature
Vegetation height	Low	Low	Low	High	High
Canopy closure	–	Low	High	High	Medium
Structural complexity	Low	Low	Low	Medium	High
Plant species numbers	Medium	High	Low	Medium	High
Bird species numbers	Medium	High	Low	Medium	High
Insect species numbers	Low	Low	Medium	High	High

(Source: after Smart and Andrews, 1985)

Glades

Natural glades are produced by windthrow or where trees grow poorly or have not been planted, such as around ponds and rock areas. Even in commercially-managed woodland, areas like this will occur from time to time. If they are not too common they can be left alone and they will naturally produce a variety of plants and attract birds and animals. Glades are easier to reach and manage if they are connected to the ride system. Purpose-cut glades can be located at ride intersections or cut into the woodland adjoining a ride. Such links also enable plants and animals to colonise glades more easily. Glades should be at least 0.1 hectare in size and have graded edges like rides to allow more light to enter. Small glades receive more light in winter if they are elongated on a north–south axis but for most of the year an east–west orientation gives most benefit. Greater light penetration is especially important for the numbers of butterflies and birds (including pheasants) as described below.

Any historic features associated with the edge, such as ancient wood banks, ditches and hedges, should be preserved and managed as described in *Practical Conservation: Boundary Habitats*. Shrub layers at the woodland edge are also important for game (see Chapter 6).

Special wildlife interests

Most of the measures described above will benefit wildlife, some groups benefiting more than others at different stages of the woodland cycle (see Table 5.3). However, woodland managers may have particular interests in animals such as badgers, birds or butterflies, and want to adopt special measures to encourage them. Some animals are managed for sporting interests, which raises several other considerations, for example woodland shape and size. Managing woodland for game is therefore covered in Chapter 6, even though existing woodland may be involved, while this section covers non-commercial species.

Insects

In general, insect species numbers are greatest in mature and over-mature mixed native broad-leaved woodland. This is because native tree species have most insects associated with them, mixtures support greater numbers of species than single stands, and larger trees provide both more food and greater structural diversity. Ponds and streams within a wood also help to increase insect diversity. Woodland butterflies are mostly associated with woodland margins, so that the more rides, glades and other spaces, the more likely they are to thrive. However, the caterpillars of each species are associated with particular food plants (see Table 5.4) and the adults require flowering plants to provide nectar in the summer. Woodland provides the richest habitat for butterflies, 30 to 40 species breeding in southern England (this number declines northwards for climatic reasons).

In many cases what appears to be a good habitat may not contain the plants needed to support a particular species. If you want to re-establish or introduce a particular insect species to a wood, the exercise should be organised and recorded properly to measure success and identify failures. The Joint Committee for the Conservation of British Insects has established a code of practice and is willing to help with such initiatives (see the *Helpful Organisations* booklet).

Management at any time of year is likely to affect insect populations due to disturbance or destruction of some part of their life cycle. The greater the length and amount of work, the greater the disturbance.

The distribution of woodland birds varies greatly and many of them also occur in more open areas, as long as hedgerows or clumps of trees are present. They also migrate between wooded and more open areas at different seasons. To

Birds

Table 5.4   A guide to woodland butterflies

Species	Food plant	Flight time	Distribution
Butterflies that usually only breed in woodland and woodland margins			
Purple emperor	Sallow	Jul–Aug	Central S England
White admiral	Honeysuckle	Jun–Aug	England south of Severn–Humber
Silver-washed fritillary	Dog violet	Jun–Aug	S and W England, Wales
High brown fritillary	Dog violet	Jun–Aug	S England, Lake District, Wales
Heath fritillary	Plantains, cow wheat	Jun–Jul	Kent, Devon, Cornwall (very local)
Pearl-bordered fritillary	Dog violet	May–Jun	S, W, NW England, Wales, central Scotland
Small pearl-bordered fritillary	Dog violet	Jun–Jul	S, W, NW England, Wales, Scotland
Wood white	Tuberous pea, vetches	May–Jun, Jul	S England, SE Wales
Speckled wood	Grasses	Apr–May, Jul–Sept	England, Wales, SW Scotland
Purple hairstreak	Oak	Jul–Aug	England, Wales, SW Scotland
Black hairstreak	Blackthorn	Jun–Jul	Central England
Butterflies that breed in hedgerows and grassland and woodland margins *			
Duke of Burgundy fritillary	Cowslip	May–Jun	S England, very local elsewhere
Comma	Hop, nettle, currant	Mar–Jun, Jul–Oct	S and central England, Wales
Brimstone	Blackthorn, alder buckthorn	Mar–Jun, Aug–Oct	England and Wales
Gatekeeper	Grasses	Jul–Sept	England, except NE, Wales
Ringlet	Grasses	Jun–Aug	Widespread S and central England, Wales, local NW England
Holly blue	Holly, ivy	Apr–May, Jul–Sept	Widespread S England and Wales, local N England
Brown hairstreak	Blackthorn	Aug–Oct	S and central England, W Wales
White-letter hairstreak	Wych elm, common elm	Jul–Aug	S and central England, Wales

* Many other grassland species can be found in woodland margins (see P589 *Practical Conservation: Grasslands, Heaths and Moors*).

Table 5.5 Habitat requirements of some widely distributed birds associated with broad-leaved woodlands

Species	Favoured stage of the forestry cycle*					Important features required†						
	Clear fell	Pre-thicket	Thicket	High forest	Over-mature	Bare soil	Litter layer	Ground/field layers	Shrub layer	Tree canopy	Trunks/branches	Snags/dead trees
Coal tit				★★	★★★		F	F	F	F	N	N
Lesser spotted woodpecker				★★	★★★					F	F/N	F/N
Pied flycatcher			★	★★	★★★			F	F	F		F/P
Wood warbler			★	★★	★★★			N	F	F		
Green woodpecker			★	★★	★★★	F	F	F			F/N	F/N
Great spotted woodpecker			★	★★	★★★					F	F/N	F/N
Marsh tit			★	★★	★★★			F	F	F		N
Nuthatch			★	★★	★★★					F	F/N	F/N
Redstart			★	★★	★★★		F	F			N	N
Tawny owl			★	★★	★★★	F	F	F			N/P	N
Jay			★★	★★	★★★		F		F/N	F		
Treecreeper		★	★★	★★	★★★				F	F	F/N	N
Sparrowhawk			★★	★★★	★★			F	F	N	N/P	
Woodcock	★	★★	★★	★★★	★★	F	F/N	F				
Hawfinch			★★	★★★	★★		F	F	F/N	F/N	P	P
Spotted flycatcher			★	★★★	★★					F	P	N/P
Chiffchaff			★	★★★	★★			N	F	F/P		
Blackcap		★	★★	★★★	★★			F	F/N	F		
Turtle dove			★★★	★★	★★	F		F	N			
Wren	★★	★★	★★★	★★	★★		N	F	F/N			
Garden warbler		★★	★★★	★★				F	F/N	F		
Long-tailed tit		★★	★★★	★★					F/N	F		
Nightingale		★★	★★★	★★					F/N			
Tree pipit	★★	★★					F	F/N		F/P	P	P
Nightjar	★★	★★				N	N					P

(Source: Smart and Andrews, 1985)
* ★ = marginal; ★★ = suitable; ★★★ = optimal.
† F = feeding; N = nesting; P = perching.

encourage birds you need to consider their feeding, nesting and territory requirements and winter survival (see Table 5.5). Harvesting of trees early in the woodland cycle denies nesting space for birds, and work in the breeding season (March to July) disturbs them. Most breeding birds finish nesting

Table 5.6 A guide to some woodland mammals

Species	Distribution	Other habitats
Grey squirrel	Widespread except N Scotland	Hedgerows, parks, gardens
Red squirrel	IoW, E Anglia, N Wales, N England, Scotland	–
Wood mouse	Widespread	Hedgerows, farmland, gardens
Yellow-necked mouse	S England, except Midlands and SW England, Wales	Hedgerows, gardens
Dormouse	England and Wales, especially coppice	Hedgerows
Fat dormouse	Chilterns	–
Fox	Widespread	Nearly all rural and urban areas
Badger	Widespread	Hedgerows, farmland, quarries, cliffs, moorland
Pine marten	Wales, Lake District, Scotland	Moorland
Red deer	Scotland, NW England, very local elsewhere	Moorland
Sika deer	SW England, W Yorkshire, Scotland	Farmland and moorland near woodland
Fallow deer	Most of England and Wales, parts of Scotland	Farmland
Roe deer	Most of Scotland, S and SW England, parts of E Anglia	Farmland
Muntjac	SE England	–

during July, except for a few species which have multiple clutches. In the north, especially Scotland, breeding starts later (April) so some flexibility is possible, although many birds begin looking for breeding places in early to mid-February, while roosting birds can be present at other times of the year.

Nesting boxes can ease the competition for nest sites for some species, but territorial behaviour limits the number of breeding birds of any one species within a woodland. A limited range of bird species thrive in pure coniferous plantations, for example long-eared owl, coal tit, goldcrest and crossbill, whereas broad-leaf plantations have a much greater variety. Mixed plantations of conifers and broad-leaves often have the most species due to the extra diversity; both the planting of broad-leaves at the edges of coniferous woods and the use of conifers as a nurse crop to broad-leaves will favour birds.

The presence of ponds or streams will also increase the number of bird species attracted to the woodland, especially wild-fowl, although they are not dependent upon the woodland itself. The presence of grassy areas around the pond encourages wildlife as does an open aspect, particularly to the south, which allows in most light.

The provision of artificial nest sites is also helpful, particularly where there are few over-mature trees. Nestboxes of varying size and design are available for a wide range of species from tawny owls to spotted flycatchers. Although nestboxes are no substitute for natural nest sites in mature or over-mature trees, they can provide important stop-gaps in young stands.

Mammals

Many mammals damage woodland trees and a few may need to be controlled where timber production is important. Most of the practices that favour other wildlife will also favour woodland mammals (see Table 5.6). Existing

populations are best conserved by minimising disturbance in the breeding season (March to July for most species), by avoiding planting on or destroying places like badger setts or fox holes and by providing gateways or flaps in perimeter fencing that can be used by animals such as badgers (these are best sited on known badger or other animal runs). Small mammals are probably at their most vulnerable in the winter, when hibernating or when food is scarce, and can suffer from activities such as coppicing.

The following list summarises the management options to improve the conservation interest of woodland margins and particular wildlife species.

▶ Maintain wide, open sunny rides or glades. Closed canopies result in fewer butterflies and birds and reduce the ground flora.

▶ Rides should not be mown frequently or in their entirety, otherwise flowers will be lost as well as valuable food plants for insects and other animals. Cut short sections only, and cut every 2 years or cut each side in alternate years, in winter if possible.

▶ Maintain a graded edge with marginal scrub. This provides structural diversity and insect food plants.

▶ Manage ponds and streams by keeping an open margin on the south side.

▶ Use broad-leaves along watercourses in coniferous plantations, avoiding beech, but not so close that the watercourse is completely shaded throughout or suffers from heavy falls of leaves.

▶ Maintain herbaceous vegetation on the banks of watercourses.

▶ Do not treat woodland as a separate habitat. The presence of adjacent flower meadows and hedgerows can be important to many birds and several butterflies.

▶ Erect bird and bat boxes and badger gates in fences wherever they are needed.

▶ Avoid disturbance to animals, especially during the bird breeding season (March–July).

Recreation

Many woodlands offer scope and opportunities for informal and formal recreational activities. These woods range from large, rural, privately-owned forests to small, urban, publicly-owned woods. Whatever the type of woodland involved, recreational activities can particularly conflict with timber production and wildlife, at a localised level (Table 4.6). It is important therefore to include recreation within the management plan and to assess the type and amount of use at the time or expected in the future.

Amount of use

There are four degrees of recreational use listed below in order of increasing usage. Not all woods will have every category.

1   Zone A – little visited (fewer than 100 people per hectare per year) because of poor access and the type of woodland.

2   Zone B – moderately used (100–1000 people per hectare per year). Mainly visited by those enjoying longer walks or wanting to do special studies or sports.

3   Zone C – well used (1000–10 000 people per hectare per year). Commonly areas of woodland within 100–200 metres of a public road or car park.

4   Zone D – very well used (more than 10 000 people per hectare per year). Mainly the edge of woodlands beside car parks and near to housing estates.

Visitor surveys are not always necessary to obtain information about the use of woodland. Simple inspection will show where most people go and, obviously, car parks and rights-of-way indicate where the main public use is likely to occur. However, the pattern and degree of use may change after management activities.

As indicated above, woodland is able to absorb large numbers of people and provide an environment for many kinds of recreational pursuit. Much of this will be informal recreation such as walking, horse riding or observing the wildlife that occurs throughout the year, although there will be seasonal peaks, most people visiting the woodland area in the summer months, and weekly peaks with more visitors at weekends.

Increasingly people are pursuing more formal, organised activities such as guided study tours, educational visits (particularly by school children), pony trekking, orienteering and survival/war games. Although often providing a greater concentration of users these organised activities are usually less frequent than informal activities.

When a wood is popular and enjoyed by many, several kinds of damage can occur:

- ▷ wear and tear of tracks and paths often leading to localised erosion;
- ▷ compaction of soil around prominent features, e.g. a noteworthy tree;
- ▷ theft of plants, holly, Christmas trees, etc.;
- ▷ disturbance of wildlife;
- ▷ walking and trampling over young seedlings and other plants;
- ▷ accidental fires.

Urban woods in particular act as dumping grounds for rubbish, which is an eyesore, and can also suffer vandalism, although most is not malicious and is an inevitable consequence of many youngsters playing in them.

Such damage is not common and can be prevented by encouraging an appreciation and understanding of the woodland and its management by both visitors and the local community – even to the extent of getting them involved in some way – and by modifying silvicultural operations to fit in with the recreational pressures. General measures to consider are:

- ▷ encourage good relations with the public;
- ▷ publicise silvicultural intentions particularly among local residents' associations, conservation groups, etc., or even involve local people directly in management committees;
- ▷ erect signs to warn of dangerous operations and, where appropriate, include on-site interpretation describing what is being done and why and/or mention it in the local press;
- ▷ avoid neatness or tidiness as these are not features of a woodland, indeed semi-natural regrowth is desirable because it has a 'wild' appearance, but remove rubbish and litter as they greatly detract from enjoyment of a wood and engender a less caring attitude on the part of the visitor;
- ▷ open up the canopy to increase enjoyment by creating glade effects and more diverse wildlife habitats;

▶ avoid practices that seem to attract damage and are especially vulnerable, most notably the planting of single trees in readily accessible open spaces. Where protection is necessary, e.g. around regeneration, use fencing that is difficult to climb over.

Most people only need or wish to use part of a large woodland area so woods can be 'zoned' according to the amount of use (as described above) and/or other objectives, such as timber production or wildlife.

Zone A – in large woods where some parts are little visited areas can be set aside solely to produce timber or to allow wildlife to flourish. Any thinning or felling operations should be confined to the winter when few visitors are expected for safety reasons. You could consider using part of this area for nature study/education or for a specific recreational activity if it occurs only infrequently.

Zone B – where the woodland is moderately used by the public some yield of timber is feasible from thinnings to maintain stand health and from regeneration operations. If the size and structure of the woodland permits, felling or coppicing should be done in small areas, up to 0.5 hectares, and fenced if necessary. In the long term, it may be possible to bring parts of zone B areas into greater use to relieve pressure on parts of a wood classified as zones C or D.

Zone C – where a woodland is well used the matter of public safety becomes especially important. Felling operations should initially be limited to the removal of unsafe trees. Large gaps can be exploited for natural regeneration by accepting any naturally-occurring seedlings or planting small groups of individually protected trees. Often there will be satisfactory regeneration in a thicket of brambles and other undergrowth; such areas should be encouraged and not cleared. Public enjoyment of the wood should be enhanced by making paths obvious, keeping them open and providing an all-weather surface and interpretation boards. Consider having a circular route through the area which, if containing items of special interest, could be way-marked and explained through trail leaflets. Most people only take short walks and usually prefer to follow a prescribed route or path for comfort and convenience.

Zone D – usually only small parts of a wood are very highly used but personal safety must be of paramount importance in them. Remove decayed branches and fell unsafe trees (see zone C above). Plant up gaps using individually protected trees. On occasion there may be benefit in planting a standard or half-standard tree but they are expensive. It may also be essential to provide public facilities such as car parks, toilets, paths, picnic areas and litter baskets as well as on-site interpretation. In the very long term you should plan to relieve pressure on zone D areas, particularly if regeneration is proving difficult, by establishing new facilities elsewhere in the wood.

5.3   Deciding on options for managing your woodland

The exercises and case study sections related to this chapter are in Sections 6.5 and 6.6, respectively.

Chapter 6

CREATING NEW WOODLAND

This chapter deals mainly with the creation of new woodland areas by adding to existing woodland or developing 'green-field' sites. Once the wood is established, its management will be the same as described in Chapters 4 and 5. However, with new woodland, there are a greater number of options for planning and designing the planting to meet specific objectives, and careful consideration is needed before deciding to plant woodland on any particular site. If you did a full integrated management plan of your holding, as described in the foundation book, you will have considered all aspects of the land area, and not just those relating to woodland or to timber production. You should only plant trees if this integrated management plan indicated that woodland was, all things considered, including landscape and wildlife conservation, the best use of the land.

write as opening paragraph

Wildlife and landscape change

When new land is planted with trees, the landscape and wildlife of that land are gradually transformed. Most of the species present in pasture, meadows or arable fields are eventually replaced by woodland-inhabiting species. The departure of grassland species takes place mainly in the first 10–20 years after planting. The young trees grow together and kill the pre-existing vegetation by shading. Some woodland species move in during this early phase, but most take 50 years or more to become established, when the woodland becomes more mature. Ecologically, the change to woodland continues for decades.

Similarly, although some management activities such as felling will have an immediate impact, others, like a newly planted wood, evolve slowly and good landscape design requires that you recognise this longer term perspective and attempt to predict how the area will look at various points in the future. The main questions to consider from a conservation point of view are:

- which sites should or should not be planted;
- how can species which are already on the site be protected;
- how can a wood with the capacity to become rich in wildlife be created;
- how can a wood be planned and designed to blend in with the landscape;
- how can woodland designed for game and recreation also provide a valuable wildlife habitat and landscape feature?

6.1   Choosing the site

The choice of a site depends upon your objectives and how they interact – do you want a commercial timber forest with landscape and wildlife appeal, a game covert that supports wildlife or a wildlife reserve that provides supporting income from firewood?

As was pointed out in Chapter 5 of the foundation book, the more you try to simplify your objectives, the more difficult it will be to incorporate conservation alongside other management activities. If you are prepared to consider more complex sets of mixed objectives, your opportunities for integrated management will be greatly increased.

Wildlife considerations

From a wildlife point of view, new woodland should be established on land which has been assessed as having little conservation value in its existing state and where the new woodland should be a considerable improvement; for example, arable or rotational grass, new wasteland or other disturbed sites (areas devoid of topsoil due to earth-moving operations and unweathered structureless substrates that occur on new waste tips).

Where not to plant

The following types of land may have a considerable existing conservation value which would be lost if the use of the land was changed:

▶ rough grazing;

▶ old unimproved grassland, which has not been ploughed for the last 10 years, not had herbicide broadcast in the last 5 years, not been regularly dressed with fertiliser or slurry and which contains a variety of non-grass species including rushes and sedges (such land is excluded from planting under the Farm Woodland Scheme except on a limited basis in the uplands);

▶ land used regularly for breeding by waders (e.g. curlew, redshank, snipe) and wintering wild-fowl, and other sites with a rich or rare flora and fauna;

▶ heathland (now a scarce habitat);

▶ derelict or waste land that has been untouched for more than 30 years (such areas are often relatively undisturbed and develop into interesting habitats).

Keeping existing features

On land which is to be planted, there may be important features worth preserving such as hedges and ponds.

Hedges will shelter a new plantation and help young trees to grow. They will already have some woodland wildlife in them, so keeping them will enable woodland species to colonise the new woodland rapidly. Avoid planting trees right up to the hedge as they will shade it and the adjacent land.

Ponds and wet patches should be retained, not drained, and trees should generally not be planted within 15 metres of their margins. Restrict taller trees to the north and east sides to let the sun in from the south and west. If natural scrub grows up beside the pond, allow some of it to develop. Periodically coppice the trees nearest the pond to retain them at a moderate height and avoid overshading.

Where possible, leave herb-rich grassland unplanted. Include such areas in rides and glades in the design of the new plantation, giving them a good chance to survive within it. Leave ancient monuments unplanted to preserve them (tree roots can cause significant damage).

Landscape considerations

A full landscape assessment, as described in Chapter 2 of the foundation book, will have provided information on potential woodland sites. In looking at the potential impact of new woodland on the landscape you also need to produce a visual analysis and several landscape designs showing the impact of woodland on the chosen sites (see Section 6.2).

The analysis and design for a new site should aim to blend boundaries into the surrounding landscape and promote a sense of continuity. In the uplands, shapes should reflect those of the main landscape features, i.e. jagged shapes in jagged landscapes, smooth shapes in smooth landscapes. In flat agricultural areas where there is a regular enclosure pattern, a more geometric layout can be planned.

New commercial woodland introduced into a lowland agricultural landscape may look out of place, especially if planted as small, regular shapes. Planting a new wood as an extension of one which already exists and in a shape which blends into the surrounding topography will create a more attractive feature.

Siting game coverts

If you are planning a new woodland for shooting, picking a site that will be attractive to game is important – the wood will be there a long time. Where a choice of sites is available, experiment first with a cover crop such as kale, to see if the birds use the site. If possible, position coverts on high ground, so that the birds will fly high above the guns. A south-facing aspect is most attractive to game and wildlife. Avoid planting at the edge of the farm or holding to encourage birds to remain on your ground. Also ensure that your new wood is within 500 metres of another area of cover so that birds can be driven from one area to another. The ideal situation is to have a central wood (with release pen) surrounded by a number of small subsidiary coverts. Birds can then be driven 'home' to the central wood.

If possible, areas of cover should be partially connected by, for example, a hedgerow or cover strip, to facilitate movement of game and other wildlife between sites. As with any habitat creation, ensure that you are not destroying a more important wildlife site in doing your work.

Recreation sites

New woodland is not as valuable for recreation as existing mature woodland. If recreation is a long-term objective you will need to think about existing or new access and the facilities to be offered in future. If the area is large or in urban areas, consider establishing the woodland over several years.

6.2   Landscape design options

To do a landscape design for new woodland, you need to be able to analyse the current landscape and to visualise how the area will look 50 years from now when the trees have matured. You do this with the help of photographs and drawings or sketches of the landscape. The drawings can be produced free-hand but you will get a more accurate impression by sketching from a photograph or transparency.

To produce a base sketch for analysis and design from a photographic transparency, project the view on to a sheet of A3 size paper and sketch in the main landform ridge lines, valleys and dominant features such as field patterns, blocks of trees and rivers. The basic outline can be photocopied as often as necessary to allow you to try out a range of design options. When adding detail

93

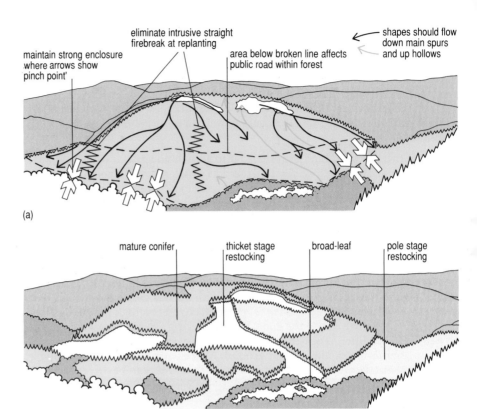

maintain strong enclosure where arrows show pinch point'

eliminate intrusive straight firebreak at replanting

area below broken line affects public road within forest

shapes should flow down main spurs and up hollows

(a)

mature conifer

thicket stage restocking

broad-leaf

pole stage restocking

(b)

Figure 6.1 Forest landscape design: (a) visual analysis – sketch of existing landscape; (b) sketch to show landscape impact of management options. (Source: Forestry Commission internal paper)

to the basic sketch use coloured pens or different texture patterns to block in the main vegetation features, as shown in Figure 6.1.

Photographic prints, especially in panoramic form, are a useful and versatile basis for analysis and design. Working and presentation sketches may be produced from them in two ways.

1   The photograph can be overlaid with a transparent acetate sheet, firmly taped down and the landscape features traced using a fine spirit-based pen. This sketch can then be photocopied for use as a design base. Photocopying the photograph itself often gives poor results.

2   A photocopier capable of reproducing half-tones is a good method of producing a base for both working and presentation drawings. It is a fast and accurate method and most of the detail is retained. Too much detail can, however, be a disadvantage when you want to predict the future effect of landscape changes.

Visual analysis

In upland areas or hilly lowland areas the first drawing will be a visual analysis, using arrows of varying strength to show lines of visual force, marking intrusive features such as rock outcrops and including comments on the character and quality of the landscape, as shown in Figures 6.1a and 6.2a. 'Visual force' is a term describing the way in which the eye perceives a landscape and is attracted to specific components within it, such as the trough of a valley, or the slope of a hill.

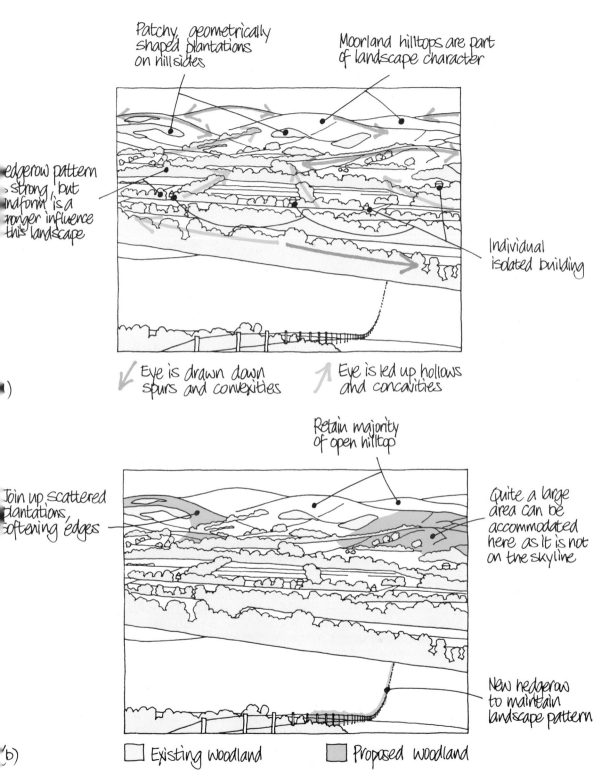

Patchy, geometrically shaped plantations on hillsides

Moorland hilltops are part of landscape character

Hedgerow pattern is strong, but landform is a stronger influence this landscape

Individual isolated building

Eye is drawn down spurs and convexities

Eye is led up hollows and concavities

(a)

Retain majority of open hilltop

Join up scattered plantations, softening 'edges'

Quite a large area can be accommodated here as it is not on the skyline

New hedgerow to maintain landscape pattern

(b)

☐ Existing woodland   ▨ Proposed woodland

Figure 6.2 (a) Visual analysis and (b) design of the landscape in Figure 2.1

95

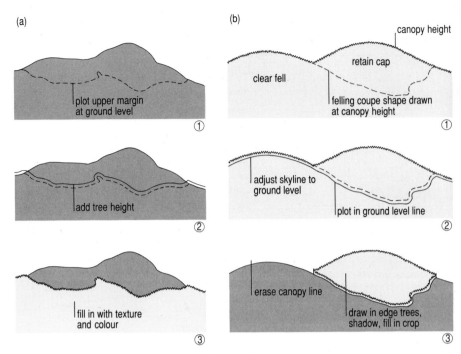

Figure 6.3 Sketches of woodland landscape changes for (a) new planting and (b) felling. (Source: Forestry Commission internal paper)

(a) labels: ① plot upper margin at ground level; ② add tree height; ③ fill in with texture and colour

(b) labels: canopy height; clear fell; retain cap; ① felling coupe shape drawn at canopy height; ② adjust skyline to ground level; plot in ground level line; ③ erase canopy line; draw in edge trees, shadow, fill in crop

Landscape designs

Figure 6.3 shows that you can obtain an accurate and realistic impression of changes in the woodland landscape brought about by both felling and planting. When designing new planting it is usual to draw the woodland margins at ground level as a dotted line and then add the eventual tree height as a solid line to provide a more realistic image of the landscape when the trees are mature. Similarly, when designing a felling pattern for existing woodland outline the shape of the felling coupe at canopy height as a dotted line and then draw the shape at ground level as a solid line to take account of tree height. In each case make any necessary adjustments at the skyline. Different areas can then be blocked in using coloured pencils or 'textured', as in Figure 6.1b, to represent conifers, broad-leaves, hedgerows, grassland and other crops, leaving felling coupes white. Always try out a number of different designs so that you, or your clients, can make a well-informed choice.

Other drawings can be used to show felling and planting patterns as a 'time series', showing different ages of plantations marked in different colours; or the species pattern in summer, winter and autumn colours.

Design considerations

In lowland designs it is important to consider concepts of shape (external edges, woodland coupe boundaries, patterns of different tree species), the scale of the area being observed and the components within it, the diversity of features and the unity (but not uniformity) of the view, so that nothing looks out of place.

The eye naturally seeks out the skyline or the presence of water in a landscape, and careful design is needed to protect and enhance their appearance. Within a large forest consider ways of reducing the uniformity of the area. For example, by avoiding planting right up to water courses, or by exposing crags and rocky knolls, these natural features are highlighted and, where soil conditions permit, the use of larch or broad-leaved species can add variety to large areas of evergreen. You can also exploit the range of shades of blue and green among different coniferous and broad-leaved species.

In the past, even where mixed species were used, planting was often done in regular patterns to prevent one species from swamping the other or to make felling easier. The result was very unnatural. By careful planning of the size and shape of felling coupes it is possible to modify a forest and realign compartments so that they integrate more readily with existing landforms. Where coupe and compartment boundaries follow natural features and clearly identifiable groups of trees can be retained, a relatively large area can be felled while maintaining or improving the overall character of the landscape. Skylines have a strong visual impact and they should be either completely open or continuous forest since isolated trees generally appear out of scale.

When replanting, take care not to introduce too much visual diversity which can be out of character with the surrounding landcape and make sure the balance between different species, or between woodland and other landscape features, is in proportion with the scale of the landscape as a whole. Restocking provides an opportunity to reshape the forest edge or to introduce drifts of contrasting species to break up an evergreen monoculture, and certain areas could remain unplanted to expose natural features.

Landscape objectives and options – summary

Landscape design options for all new woodland should attempt to satisfy the following objectives:

▷ to blend sympathetically with, and reflect the form of, the land;

▷ to minimise intrusive effects;

▷ to enhance visually important natural features such as gullies and crags;

▷ to avoid unnatural straight lines, regularity or geometrical patterns and shapes;

▷ to be of a scale appropriate to the landform;

▷ to integrate visually with adjacent farmland and become increasingly irregular near to water;

▷ to encourage diversity in species, ages and stand composition.

Among the options for achieving these objectives in commercial coniferous forest are:

▷ ensure a good match of species with site so that the trees will grow;

▷ use broad-leaves to emphasise the natural landform in gullies and near watercourses;

▷ plant in irregular shapes related to landform and avoid straight edges;

▷ aim for simplicity and appropriate scale;

▷ make use of or augment existing broad-leaved trees and woodland, e.g. on exposed crags or along a lower boundary to link with hedgerows.

For scenically uninteresting new coniferous and broad-leaved plantations, avoid spotted, striped or chequered patterns by:

▷ not planting in strips;

▷ varying the number of trees, shapes and separation of groups in group planting, or using a roughly diamond pattern if a more organised layout is absolutely necessary.

6.3   Designing a wildlife-rich wood

When a site has been chosen as suitable for planting trees and you have decided on the area to be planted, based on an integrated management plan and a landscape design, you also need to think about ways of maximising the wildlife interest of the wood. At the planting stage, the most important aspect to consider is species selection.

Other options that will improve the eventual wildlife interest of the wood are:

▶   planting next to an existing established wood or linking two or more existing plantings;

▶   planting areas over 5 hectares;

▶   planting native trees and shrubs;

▶   planting a mixture of tree species and/or staggering the planting to produce uneven-aged stands;

▶   planting shrub as well as tree species;

▶   managing woodland margins to provide the greatest available diversity and light;

▶   using irregular and/or graded edges for rides and glades;

▶   avoiding the widespread use of herbicides by spot treatment or by using **tree shelters**, biodegradable plastic mulch or mechanical or hand weeding where necessary (note that the vegetation will be killed off by all the methods if not eventually by the trees and that spot-treatment by herbicides may be the best option);

▶   thinning the trees at the thicket stage to avoid heavy shading of the woodland floor.

Species selection

Where wildlife conservation is a major objective, a mixture of tree species native to the locality should be planted to provide the greatest possible ecological diversity and naturalness. Table 6.1 and Figure 6.4 indicate the type of site where native trees and shrubs will grow well (see also Table 6.2 in the foundation book) and in which areas of the country they are likely to grow well and should be encouraged.

Species should always be matched with the site conditions, in particular the climate, topography and soil type. In general, exposure to wind and cold are a major constraint to the establishment of broad-leaved trees on land above 300 metres (although they do grow above this altitude through natural regeneration). Otherwise, you need to consider: whether soils are derived from chalk, limestone or sand (generally light) or from clay (generally heavy); how wet they are; and whether they are acid (some sandy soils and peat), neutral (most clay soils) or alkaline (chalk and limestone). On impoverished sites, especially waste tips, nitrogen-fixing species such as alder may be particularly valuable to aid establishment.

From the wildlife point of view you should choose strains of native species that grow locally. This helps to ensure that they will grow successfully in the area and to maintain the regional and local character of native 'treescapes', with representative combinations of trees and shrubs and their associated wildlife. Following up this suggestion on a local scale will encourage natural diversity on a national scale and minimise the degree to which habitats are colonised by introduced species or by native trees and shrubs beyond their natural range.

Table 6.1 The ideal site conditions and appropriate zones (see Figure 6.4) for native species of trees and shrubs

Species*	Site condition: Wet	Light dry soils	Heavy soils	Acid soils	Neutral or alkaline soils	Exposed	Zone: † 1	2	3	4	5	6	7	8	9	10
+ Alder, black	★				★		●	●	●	●	●	●	●	●	●	●
+ Ash	★	★	★		★	★	●	●	●	●	●	●	●	●	●	●
+ Aspen (zones 1–3)		★		★	★	★	●	●	●							
+ Aspen (zones 4–10)			★		★					●	●	●	●	●	●	●
+ Beech		★		★	★	★							●	●	●	
+ Birch, downy	★	★	★	★	★	★	●	●	●	●	●	●		●	●	●
+ Birch, silver	★	★	★	★	★	★	●	●	●	●	●	●	●	●	●	●
□ Blackthorn	★	★	★		★	★	●	●	●	●	●	●		●	●	●
□ Box		★			★									○	○	
□ Broom		★		★		★	●	●	●		●	●	●	●	●	●
□ Buckthorn, alder	★			★	★					○	○	○	○	○	○	○
□ Buckthorn, purging			★		★					○	○	○	○	○	○	○
□ Butchers broom				★	★							●	●	●	●	○
□ Cherry, bird	★				★		●	●	●	●		●				
+ Cherry, gean			★		★			●	●	●	●	●	●	●	●	●
+ Crab apple		★	★		★					○	●	●	●	●	●	●
□ Dogwood		★	★		★						●	●	●	●	●	●
□ Elder		★	★		★			●	●	●	●	●	●	●	●	●
+ Elm, wych		★			★	★	●	●	●	●	●	●	●	●	●	●
□ Gorse		★		★	★	★	●	●	●	●	●	●	●	●	●	●
□ Guelder rose	★		★		★		●	●	●	●	●	●	●	●	●	●
□ Hawthorn, common		★	★	★	★	★	●	●	●	●	●	●	●		●	●
+ Hawthorn, midland		★			★						○	○	○	○		
□ Hazel		★	★		★		●	●	●	●	●	●	●	●	●	●
□ Holly		★		★	★		●	●	●	●	●	●	●	●	●	●
+ Hornbeam		★	★		★								●	●		
□ Juniper		★		★	★	★	○	○	○	○			○	○		
+ Lime, small-leaved (zone 4)		★			★					○						
(zones 5–9)		★	★	★	★						○	○	○	○	○	
+ Lime, large-leaved		★			★					○	○		○			
+ Maple, field		★			★					○	●	●	●		●	●
+ Oak, common	★		★	★	★	★		●	●	●	●	●	●	●	●	●
+ Oak, sessile		★		★	★	★		●	●	●	●	●	●	●	●	●
+ Pine, Scots		★		★		★			○							
+ Poplar, black	★		★		★						○	○	○	○	○	
□ Privet		★			★	★					●	●	●	●	●	●
□ Rose, dog		★	★		★		●	●	●	●	●	●	●	●	●	●
□ Rose, field		★	★		★					●	●	●	●	●	●	●
+ Rowan		★		★		★	●	●	●	●	●	●	●	●	●	●
+ Service tree			★	★	★						○	○	○	○	○	○
□ Spindle			★		★						●	●	●	●	●	●
□ Wayfaring tree		★	★		★							●		●	●	●
+ Whitebeam (zones 4 and 8)		★			★	★				○				○		
+ Whitebeam (zone 7)		★		★	★	★							○			
□ Willow, almond	★				★						●	●	●	●		
□ Willow, bay	★				★				○	○						
+ Willow, crack	★				★	★			●	●	●	●	●	●	●	●
+ Willow, goat	★				★	★	●	●	●	●	●	●	●	●	●	●
+ Willow, grey	★		★		★	★	●	●	●	●	●	●	●	●	●	●
+ Willow, osier	★				★		●	●	●	●	●	●	●	●	●	●
□ Willow, purple	★				★	★				●	●	●	●	●	●	●
+ Willow, white	★				★	★				●	●	●	●	●	●	●
+ Yew		★			★					○			○	○		

(Source: after Soutar and Peterken, 1989)

* + = large and medium size trees; □ = small trees and shrubs.

† ● = planting stock should, but need not be, of local origin; ○ = planting stock should *always* be of local origin.

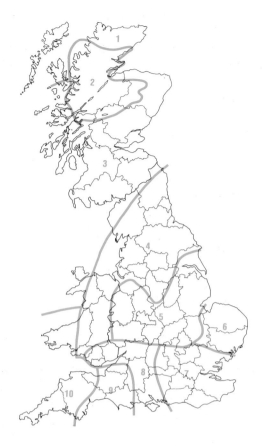

Figure 6.4   Zones providing good growing conditions for the species in Table 6.1. (Source: G. Peterken, personal communication)

Sometimes it is difficult to find plants of local provenance in the species you want. One solution in such cases is to collect local seed from within 16 kilometres of the areas to be planted, grow it in a nursery bed and plant it out on the woodland site after 2 or 3 years. This may seem like a long delay if you are anxious to make progress quickly but in the long term, given that trees of local stock are likely to grow faster than those brought in from other areas, you will probably be better off. It may be a much cheaper option than buying in trees from a nursery.

You may also be able to find **wildings**, naturally occurring seedlings. Trees produce far more seedlings than ever survive to maturity so by taking some of them you will not significantly affect natural regeneration. Wildings can therefore be a useful source of material for small scale plantings, but you should always ask the landowner's permission before taking them.

Given the extent to which species of non-local provenance have already been planted all over the country, it is not safe to assume that local seed or wildings will give you what you are looking for. The more natural, and less managed, the location, the more likely it is that seed and wildings will be of local provenance.

When trees are being produced commercially for timber, it is better to use nursery stock, of known genetic and commercial quality (see Chapter 7). Indeed the regulations governing many grant schemes specify the origin of the planting material. In broad-leaved woodland many of the suitable species will be natives, but not of local provenance, and most of the conifers used commercially are not native.

If possible, mixtures of species should be used in commercial woodland. The most useful broad-leaved mixtures for timber production, depending on the site, are:

▶ ash with alder or sycamore;

▶ beech with cherry;

▶ oak with alder, ash, cherry or sweet chestnut.

Where a broad-leaf/conifer mix is grown, compatible mixtures, site permitting, are:

▶ ash with European larch or Norway spruce;

▶ beech with Lawsons cypress, western red cedar, Scots and Corsican pines;

▶ oak with European larch, Norway spruce or Scots pine.

The ultimate value of the woodland crop depends on the factors discussed in Chapter 4.

Site disturbance

Most land suitable for establishing broad-leaves in lowland areas will be relatively fertile and rich in herbaceous weeds and climbers. It may also suffer from deer browsing or rabbit and squirrel problems. Clearing debris, controlling weeds and protecting young trees from browsing will be important but it will rarely be necessary to plough, fertilise or drain the site.

On heavy clays or peaty soils, especially in upland areas, the site often needs to be ploughed and drained before trees can be established. This can cause serious problems on peaty soils with acid run-off into streams, rivers and lakes or lochs (see Box 4.1 in the foundation book).

Long-term maintenance

Some losses after planting are almost inevitable, due to bad handling, pest attack or weed competition and some trees may need to be replaced (beating up) if losses are high (greater than one in five plants) and timber production is a primary objective. Otherwise, once established, the wood should be treated like an existing wood (see Chapters 4 and 5).

Wildlife options – summary

In order to maximise the possible wildlife conservation benefits of new woodland, follow these guidelines:

▶ only native tree species, usually of local provenance, should be planted when timber production is not an objective;

▶ where timber production is important use broad-leaf and broad-leaf/conifer mixtures in lowland areas;

▶ plant species suited to the site and within their known distribution;

▶ give special attention to native trees and shrubs such as hazel, hawthorn and holly, which are unlikely to be planted for commercial purposes;

▶ consider establishing a coppice with standards or rotational system to provide structural diversity;

> incorporate rides, glades and other open areas to provide grassland habitat;

> retain ponds, rocky outcrops and other features within the woodland area and do not plant trees too close to them.

6.4   Designing woodland for game

In addition to the aspects of woodland design and management already discussed, an important objective for game management is to present animals to the gun in a safe way, usually at defined locations. This means both providing an environment to facilitate shooting and providing conditions to ensure reproduction, growth and protection of the animals, which in woodland are generally game birds, deer and sometimes wild-fowl. Before you can manage a game species successfully, you need to understand its behaviour.

Shelter

Pheasants

The most important woodland gamebird is the pheasant, though in the uplands black grouse (black game) and capercaillie are locally important. (Partridge and red grouse are agricultural and moorland birds respectively.)

Pheasants are predominantly birds of the woodland edge, spending 70% of their time within 20 metres of open ground, although they do move out into adjacent, often agricultural, land in the summer. They do not like draughty woods and a shrubby ground cover up to 2 metres high, with a perimeter hedge, particularly on windward sides, provides warmth and shelter. Too dense a canopy will suppress the ground and shrub layers, and produce a 'cold' forest floor. Careful thinning of trees to allow light penetration, planting trees that cast light shade (for example oak or ash) and planting shade-tolerant

Table 6.2   Trees and shrubs for gamebirds

Species	Game and wildlife value
Native large deciduous trees	
Oak	Acorns eaten by pheasant and other wildlife. High insect value
Ash	Fruits eaten by pheasant. Light shade encourages understorey
Beech	Mast eaten by pheasant and other wildlife
Birch	Seeds eaten by pheasant. Light shade encourages understorey. High insect value
Exotic large deciduous trees	
Poplar	Produces high-flying birds if planted on edge of covert. Important food source for insect larvae
Larch	Excellent for roosting, especially if sheltered by evergreens. Produces high-flying birds if planted on edge of covert

Species	Game and wildlife value
Native small deciduous trees	
Field maple	Coppices well to form shrub layer
Wild cherry	Fruits relished by birds
Crab apple	Fruits of value to game and other wildlife
Rowan	Berries taken by pheasant and other birds
Bird cherry	Cover species. Fruits eaten by birds
Native evergreen trees	
Scots pine	Winter roosting cover
Yew	Winter roosting cover. Snow-free feeding points. Berries taken by birds
Exotic evergreen trees	
Cypress (Lawson and Leyland)	Perimeter shelter around wood. Early spring nesting sites
Western red cedar	Perimeter shelter
Norway spruce	Good for perimeter shelter and internal roosting sites
Western hemlock	Excellent roosting tree
Douglas fir	Good for roosting. Favoured by small passerines
Native shrubs	
Hawthorn	Berries taken by pheasant and other birds. High insect value
Wild privet	Good cover species. Fruit taken by birds
Guelder rose	Berries taken by pheasant and other birds
Dogwood	Cover species
Hazel	Cover species. Birds and mammals eat nuts
Wayfaring-tree	Cover species. Berries taken by birds
Broom	Good cover on open sites
Willow	Good, rapidly-produced cover. Food for many insects
Exotic shrubs	
Shrub honeysuckle	Winter cover but also invasive
Cotoneaster spp.	Winter cover and berries eaten by pheasant
Common laurel	Winter cover under canopy

(Source: BASC)

shrubs such as laurel are helpful, and a general scattering of shrubs throughout the covert is preferable to continuous blocks. Many trees and shrubs also provide food in the form of seeds, berries and insects (see Table 6.2). Native species are best for wildlife and landscape. However, for some requirements such as evergreen shelter, shade-tolerant shrubs, establishment in areas with heavy deer or rabbit grazing and difficult soils you may need to use introduced species. Avoid invasive species like rhododendron, snowberry and shrubby honeysuckles which will eventually make the ground cover too thick, reducing the conservation value and making it difficult to flush the birds. Only use introduced species if no native species fits the requirements and always avoid planting introduced species in ancient woodland.

Food

In addition to berry-producing shrubs, grain can be provided directly to pheasants from a hopper or by scattering it on an area covered with straw. This grain will also be eaten by squirrels and the feeding area will become severely trampled in time while the straw reduces the ground flora where it is spread. Where possible, a small part of an adjacent field can be used to grow mustard or kale within which the pheasants can forage.

Protection

Successful rearing of pheasants requires protection from predators. Crows, jays and magpies will take the eggs and foxes will take birds. If these animal predators need to be controlled, do not use poison baits or traps which are illegal. They should be shot or snared with permission from 'authorised' persons, who are the owners or occupiers of the land.

Disturbance

Disturbance of gamebirds affects their rearing success, and the presence of people and dogs must be minimised. Where there is public access, the scope for rearing pheasants will be reduced. Forestry operations also disturb gamebirds and if possible should take place outside the nesting or shooting seasons or in parts of the wood not being used for pheasant rearing.

Size and shape of woodland coverts

While smaller coverts of around 2 hectares have the highest densities of pheasants, any size of woodland can be suitable for game if well planned. Narrow areas of woodland (about 50 metres wide) are best as they require fewer beaters and are more easily driven. Although linear woods provide more 'edge' per acre of woodland there is some conflict with wildlife conservation in that very narrow woods lose much of their woodland character and few truly woodland birds will breed. There is merit, therefore, in making the wood no less than 50 metres wide. Wider woods can be broken up with rides to facilitate beating and to create extra edges for the birds. In upland woods the most common requirements to improve sporting potential are to diversify structure and to introduce broad-leaved species in what will usually be areas of pure conifer. The idea of 'game strips' is a useful one and involves planting broad-leaved species or, if impractical, pine and larch, in an irregular strip along a contour between areas of spruce. Encouraging regrowth of broad-leaved vegetation along the edges of firebreaks is also beneficial. Similarly, when roads are made in upland plantations, usually just before the time of first thinning, the sporting interest will be enhanced if the total width of road and verge is at least 25 metres and if broad-leaved species are encouraged along the verge.

Perimeter shelter

To cut off wind at the edge of a wood, a perimeter hedge of thorn and, if necessary, honeysuckle can be planted to give protection at ground level. It does not need to be very high (1.5 metres) but it should be cut to an 'A' shape so that it is thick at the base. In upland areas tree hedges of cypress, spruce or beech can be used. It is essential that these are topped at 2–3 metres otherwise

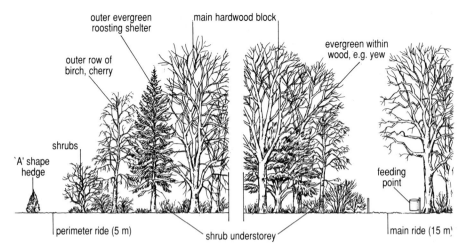

Figure labels:
- outer evergreen roosting shelter
- main hardwood block
- evergreen within wood, e.g. yew
- outer row of birch, cherry
- shrubs
- 'A' shape hedge
- feeding point
- perimeter ride (5 m)
- shrub understorey
- main ride (15 m)

Figure 6.5   Cross-section of an ideal game covert. (Source: BASC)

they become bare and draughty at the base. A 5 metre ride should separate the perimeter hedge from the first row of trees to prevent shading of the hedge and adjacent crops, to allow access for a flail to cut the hedge and to leave room for a shrubby nesting area to develop (see Figure 6.5). High shelter for roosting birds can be provided by several rows of evergreens around the wood's perimeter. Birds will either roost in these or, if the cover is too dense, in deciduous trees behind them. In large coverts, it is useful to scatter a few blocks of evergreens throughout the wood to provide internal roosting shelter (Figure 6.6). These blocks will also provide snow-free areas for feeding points. On exposed sloping sites, several evergreen belts may need to be planted across the prevailing wind to provide shelter all the way through the covert. An outer row of conifers can look unsightly. To solve this problem plant deciduous species on the outside of the wood to form a screen, keeping conifer belts and blocks within the wood.

Edge and openness

Pheasants like light and they will desert a dark, enclosed wood for an alternative where they can feed with the sun on their backs. This can be avoided by making rides as wide (and plentiful) as possible: main rides should be 15–20 metres wide and subsidiaries over 5 metres wide. In neglected woods, overgrown rides should be opened up and new rides cut. As many as possible should run in a north–south direction to catch winter sunlight. Small bays off the main ride will provide sheltered feeding sites. The rides should not be straight, to avoid creating a wind tunnel (Figure 6.6). Rides should be cut after the pheasant hatching season to produce a short turf, suitable as a drying out area. Delaying mowing until August will encourage wild flowers. Broad-leaved species such as oak and birch allow plenty of light to reach the ground layer. Some broad-leaves such as sycamore, beech and chestnut cast a dense shade and should be avoided.

Flushing areas

Provision should be made for easy flushing on the shooting day (Figure 6.7). The ideal situation is for the birds to take flight while inside the wood and be at tree height when flying over the guns. The main requirement is an area where birds can easily break out of the wood – pheasants are poor fliers and will be exhausted if they have to force their way through dense canopy. The ideal is to have areas of low cover, with open access for take-off, scattered at suitable

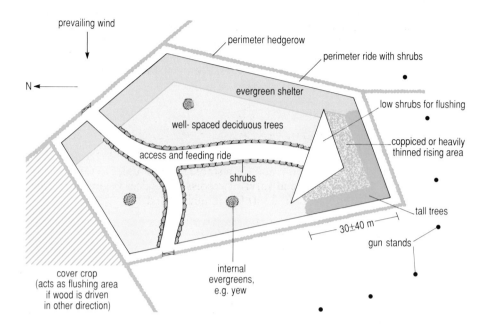

prevailing wind

perimeter hedgerow

perimeter ride with shrubs

N ←

evergreen shelter

low shrubs for flushing

well- spaced deciduous trees

coppiced or heavily thinned rising area

access and feeding ride

shrubs

30±40 m

tall trees

gun stands

cover crop
(acts as flushing area
if wood is driven
in other direction)

internal
evergreens,
e.g. yew

Figure 6.6   Planting plan for a new game covert. (Source: BASC)

points throughout the wood. This prevents a single heavy flush at the end of a drive. If the wood has little cover a special flushing area, about 30–40 metres back from the wood edge, should be incorporated into the design. Low-growing shrubs will encourage birds to squat down before flushing when the beaters arrive. Taller species can be regularly coppiced.

Flushing areas can be designed as a triangle or 'D' shape (with the apex towards the guns) so that the beaters close up as they move through the area (Figure 6.6). A rising area can also be incorporated (an area of medium height shrubs, about 4 metres high), beyond the flushing point to allow birds to rise at a gentle angle.

It is usually about 10 years before trees and shrubs make sufficient growth to hold pheasants and it is often only when protective rabbit netting is removed from the perimeter that the pedestrian pheasant uses such plantations to the full.

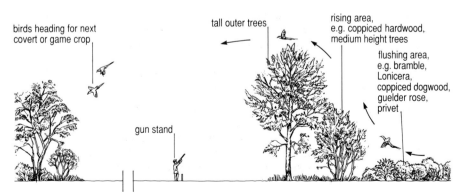

birds heading for next
covert or game crop

tall outer trees

rising area,
e.g. coppiced hardwood,
medium height trees

flushing area,
e.g. bramble,
Lonicera,
coppiced dogwood,
guelder rose,
privet

gun stand

Figure 6.7   Cross-section of a flushing area. (Source: BASC)

A new technique developed by the Game Conservancy avoids the need for fencing by using individual tree guards against rabbits, hares and, if necessary, deer. It also uses a cover crop between the tree rows to provide shelter for game. Shooting can then begin within 1 year. For the small narrow woods suitable for game, tree guards are often more economic than fencing. In addition, the extra years of shooting provide an important financial incentive.

Instant spinney

Deer

Deer management needs to strike a balance between the benefits to be obtained from hunting and the need to control numbers to avoid damage to woodland.

Culling and stalking

Good herd management should aim for a stable ratio of males to females and old to young. The birth rate and survival success of the deer in any given area must be regularly monitored and surplus animals culled.

Culling deer to control numbers will not entirely prevent the browsing of young trees and where a crop is being planted or naturally regenerated either deer fencing or individual tree protection will be needed. Open spaces are attractive to deer and are common feeding sites, so rides, glades or young crops allow safe sight lines for shooting them. High seats can be erected at such locations for this purpose. If glades do not exist they can be created. Shooting for selective control seldom means simply eliminating the sick and unhealthy, as these are infrequent in most populations unless density has risen to very high levels. If the improvement of antler quality is the objective it may be valuable to leave male deer (especially the younger animals) with the most desirable size and shape of antlers.

Woodland design

In new broad-leaved woodland or upland coniferous forest, solid blocks divided by relatively narrow rides or firebreaks are likely to harbour deer in larger numbers than the trees can stand, and the stalker may be unable to manage them properly. Birch, willow, ash and low-growing shrubs can be encouraged along the woodland edge and will relieve browsing and grazing pressure on the commercial crop. Gaps, clearings, unplanted areas, natural open avenues like the courses of streams, wider rides and forest roads with unplanted verges all give the deer access to areas where they can enjoy the warmth of direct sunlight and feed on the vegetation along the forest edge.

6.5   Deciding on options for managing your woodland

Having read in Chapter 5 about the range of options that can be adopted to improve the conservation value of existing woodland, you should now decide which are most appropriate for the area you are studying. Remember to base the decision on your integrated assessment and on a careful consideration of the land manager's objectives. Section 6.6 gives some examples from the two case studies.

You should not decide to plant any new woodland on your own case study area without first doing a full integrated management plan. If this has been done and it indicates that planting woodland is the best option, plan the area of planting and the species mix according to landscape design and wildlife considerations, as described in this chapter.

6.6 Options for managing existing and for planting new woodland in the case study areas

Killiehangie Hill, Atholl Estate

The integrated assessment identified the severe, and probably continuing, problem of deer-damage to Norway spruce on Killiehangie Hill, and at the same time a need to improve the structural and species diversity of the woodland for both landscape and wildlife reasons. The following options were considered.

Option 1

Continue as at present, removing the more severely damaged trees when thinning. The likely result of this would be a rapid decline of Norway spruce, loss of increment and revenue, loss of markets due to a fall in the standard of product, 'snap' of trees at stripping height (about 1 metre), build up of bark borers and weevil, windblow devastation, loss of money, a huge loss of growing time and an increased fire hazard.

Benefits would include the break-up of age class and a change in ground vegetation followed by an increase in birds and animals feeding on seeding weeds and insects.

Option 2

Thin to remove all damaged trees and continue deer control.

The likely result would be an initial improvement in appearance but this would be short-lived and too dramatic a change for the remaining Norway spruce. Windblow, further deer damage and a rapid decline would continue, much as for Option 1.

Option 3

This option had several components.

1   Clear-cut two or three patches of the more severely damaged sections. Net income on this operation, for 12 hectares, would be approx. £12 000 (sold standing) chiefly for chipwood.

2   Fence off the western boundary to discourage deer movement. (This cannot be guaranteed absolutely as snow can build up against the fence in winter, and trees can fall across it, allowing the deer access.) This would require about 1.5 kilometres of deer fence, costing approximately £7000.

3   Attempt to shoot out totally the red deer (chiefly overwintering stags which have reverted to their status as woodland creatures).

4   Improve road access and make modest clearings to assist deer control.

5   Leave felled areas bare for probably two or three seasons, both to assist in deer control and as a natural control against pests such as *Hylobius* beetle.

6   Fence felled areas separately against red deer, roe deer, hares and rabbits.

7   Replant with a change of species – Sitka spruce, Douglas fir, Scots pine, hybrid larch – which are more or less untouched by deer. Include some birch, oak and wild and bird cherry, also less likely to be damaged. Some conifer butt rot is beginning to appear and a change of species is also indicated for this reason.

8   At all times in the future, leave some of the older Norway spruce as a control together with willow as a 'honeypot' in times of deer break-in, for example, after storms.

Sell some of the stags for sporting income. This would be slow and costly and would get in the way of necessary forest operations. If option 3 is adopted, an opportunity for roe deer stalking will arise in a year or two as they like low cover. *Option 4*

Option 3 was the one advised to the owner, because of the possibility of regaining commercial viability and of improving wildlife and landscape conservation. It was decided to follow it.

The fencing is well under way and the deer are being successfully controlled. Revenue from clear cutting (poor value timber) and from cutting along lines will cover the cost of boundary fencing, some of the road work and the fencing and planting costs of cleared areas. However, this is a cost-saving operation only. It does not cover initial investment costs and subsequent maintenance of the forested area, which has been cut down just as it was reaching the stage where it generates revenue. *Implementation*

1   Severe disruption to overall planning, management time and programme of work. *The costs*

2   Considerable loss of increment and income.

3   Increase in working costs.

4   Costly in time – applying for felling licence and considering landscape requirements.

1   Break up of age class and introduction of structural diversity. (The manager would have preferred to do this in a more carefully planned and controlled manner.) *Benefits*

2   Increase in conservation value (flora and fauna) and in sporting value.

3   More views and vistas.

4   A new fence for our neighbour!

Given that the Norway spruce is 40% of this stand and that 50% of it is eventually clear-cut prematurely, at say 60% of its paper standing value at that time, the loss of increment and sawlog value assumes a less disastrous perspective. Also, the area of Norway spruce to be clear felled is less than 1% of the estate forest land.

If the action taken is successful, in many respects a 'better hill' will result.

Thinning began with a buoyant market, but later sawmills and pulpmills were over-supplied, as a result of a spring windblow and a mild winter allowing more work than usual to continue.

At present sawlogs, pallet wood and small wood for chip pulp are difficult to sell, and it would be a commercial error to offer parcels for tender, although this may have to be done in the case of Killiehangie.

Small woods in Sussex

The outcome of the integrated assessment was the production of a Woodland Grant Scheme plan for submission to and approval by the Forestry Commission. The plan has the following features. *Existing woodland*

1   *Timber production* – the timber currently has little value due to its poor quality and a depressed timber market. The option of on-site processing using a mobile band saw has been discussed but no decision yet made. The coppice

and **underwood** could be used for firewood and stakes for hedge-laying. A proposed sweet chestnut plantation will be used for fencing on the farm.

2   *Landscape* – the farm lies within the Sussex Downs AONB and the woods are important landscape features looking both from the Downs and towards them. The plan aims to retain the essential broad-leaved character of the woodland.

3   *Wildlife* – four of the woods are ancient and contain a number of unusual plants and animals. The plan recognises this by leaving large parts of the woodland alone. Features to encourage wildlife are included, for example ride creation, glades, pond creation and the leaving of dead wood and mature trees.

4   *Storm damage* – in deference to wildlife needs there is no random clearance of storm-damaged areas; natural regeneration will take place in these areas.

5   *Educational resources* – the farm's woods have already been used for survey work and consideration is being given to develop one of them as a demonstration woodland. With heavy public access on the farm there is also the opportunity to improve the farming image.

Other options considered but then rejected were as follows.

1   *Game/shooting* – heavy public access would create problems although the potential income return would be high. The construction of release pens and the feeding of birds could be damaging to the ancient woodland flora.

2   *Alternatives to agricultural production* – the timber value of the existing woods is very low whilst the financial incentives offered for new planting under the Farm Woodland Scheme are not sufficient to interest the farm manager.

Broadly the plan covers the following management proposals.

1   Two of the smallest woods have no management recommendations but this can be reviewed in 5 years' time.

2   Two other small woods have utilisable timber, some of which will be felled and replanted with broad-leaves. Some trees will be thinned to promote the growth of promising stems.

3   The two biggest woods have programmes of clear and selective felling (including coppicing) followed by replanting with native broad-leaves; some areas will be thinned whilst a block of now useless conifers will be removed and replanted with broad-leaves (Plumpton Wood). Access within one of the woods (Plumpton Wood) has been improved recently by the clearance of old rides and this will also be necessary in the other wood.

The main constraints in actually getting this work done are as follows.

1   Access to most of the woods is good but only one has good access for machinery within it. Even then, being on heavy soils, the ground is very wet in winter and timber extraction could be difficult. This problem has been compounded in some cases by the profusion of fallen timber following the 1987 hurricane.

2   It should be possible to divert some farm labour into the woodlands in the winter but there can be no guarantee of this. With little experience of woodland work it is vital that they receive adequate training (particularly in safety) and that they are given very specific instructions on what to do. Some of the proposed work may well be beyond farm staff capabilities and contractors will need to be brought in.

3   Finances, which fall into two problem areas.

(a)   The grant under the Woodland Grant Scheme is for planting only and is given in instalments after the work is done. Thus the costs of felling and replanting will have to be covered initially by the farm and the grant reclaimed later. It is estimated that the grant for planting will cover about half of the costs incurred although the use of farm labour will reduce the cost.

(b)   The returns on the felled timber and underwood are uncertain but are unlikely to be high. They could be improved if on-farm conversion using a mobile band-saw were used. However, the commitment of the farm manager to do something and the advice and encouragement he has received from all concerned means that these constraints will not prevent the plan being implemented to some degree.

The plan runs until 1993 when it can be renewed. There are no penalties if none or only a part of the job is done but the grant is only given for the planting which actually takes place.

New woodland is not considered to be a viable option at this time on the farm, *New woodlands* with little land surplus to the farming business needs. The main exception is the scrub area around Beech Wood which, although valuable for birds, has encroached on to previously flower-rich grassland. Visually, it is mainly the internal landscape that matters since the area is not prominent within the plain.

Ironically, this part of the farm falls within the South Downs ESA and would be eligible for grant aid if it were returned to herb-rich grassland but not woodland. The farm manager has therefore decided that this area should be enhanced as grassland, to provide additional grazing. The current low value of the site for most wildlife might have improved naturally as a succession developed but this was a case where both business and conservation objectives had to be integrated.

Chapter 7

IMPLEMENTATION AND MONITORING

Once you have a clear idea of which management options are feasible on your land, based on your assessment of its quality and potential, the options you choose to put into practice will depend on your objectives and the constraints affecting your use of the land, as described in the foundation book.

If you are unclear or uncertain of what action to take at this, or at any other, stage in the management planning process, it is important to seek professional advice or help. This is most important when the outcomes of the management plan are being transferred to a detailed work plan, describing when and where operations are to be done, who will do the work, the equipment needed, the expected costs and benefits and how the results are to be monitored in the long term.

Both a management plan and a work plan should be written before any work is done. Not only will this help clarify the objectives for the planner it will also provide agreed guidelines for the workforce, whether they be your own labour or contractors brought in to do the job. Equally important, grant aid is usually approved on the submission of an appropriate management/work plan and normally before any work is undertaken.

7.1   Grant aid

Each grant-aiding organisation (see the *Helpful Organisations* booklet) has its own grant conditions. These are designed to ensure that the project is done correctly and that the recipient will fulfil the objectives of the grant-awarding body. You must clearly understand these conditions before applying for grant aid and particularly check whether prior approval is needed for any work. If work has started, the grant aid may be forfeited.

Although there may be several potential sources of grant aid for any one project, it is generally the case that they are mutually exclusive, i.e. only one grant can be given for an individual project. However, there are exceptions to this. For example, in National Parks additional payments may be available from the National Park Authority to supplement grants under Ministry of Agriculture, Fisheries and Food (MAFF) schemes. Similarly, a management grant from MAFF may be available to supplement Forestry Commission grants for new woodland planting on agricultural land.

Taxation

The taxation position of woodlands is continually changing and you should consult a financial adviser about it. As of 1988, commercial woodlands have been removed from the scope of income tax and corporation tax. Special rules which tend to favour woodlands often apply to capital gains and inheritance tax.

7.2 Woodland management costs

The major direct costs of woodland management are labour and materials, but equipment and the timing of operations will also be important. For example, you may have spare labour available at particular times of the year, which would allow you to cut the cost of some operations or you may find that a winch fitted to a farm tractor is sufficient to extract timber. However, there are also indirect costs in necessary items such as training, insurance and the management costs due to grant and planning procedures.

Labour

Woodlands are long-lived crops and the level of labour required varies enormously between operations and throughout the complete woodland cycle (see Table 7.1). Establishment and harvesting are the most time-consuming

Table 7.1 Typical woodland operations and their labour requirement

Operation	Typical output/day
Work for which training is not essential — confined to some kinds of work done with hand tools	
Brashing*	100 trees
Cleaning – other than use of clearing saw	0.1 ha
Coppicing of small-size material grown on short rotation for stick products	0.02 ha
Pruning*	30 trees
Weeding, hand only*	0.03 ha
Work for which training is highly desirable or which must be well supervised by a knowledgeable person	
Cleaning* with clearing saw	0.25 ha
Fencing*	30–50 m
Marking and measuring trees for thinning	2 ha
Planting* including beating up, enrichment, etc.	600 trees
Weeding	
mechanical* (tractor mounted)	1–2 ha
application of herbicide (use of weed wipers, granular applicators)	1.5–2 ha
Work which, for reasons of safety and quality of workmanship, must only be done by trained operators or by competent contractors	
Coppicing with chainsaw	0.05 ha
Felling trees*, including **snedding***	3.5 tonnes
Extraction of trees and logs (tractors)	15 tonnes

(Source: MAFF, 1986)

* Forestry work has a high industrial accident rate. This operation is subject to recommendations for safe working practice set out in the *Forest Industry Safety Guides* published by the Forestry Safety Council. These guides are sent free on application.

Table 7.2 A suggested calendar for woodland work

Month	Operation
September	Site preparation for spring planting. Clearance, drainage, fencing, etc.
October	Harvesting – coppice-cutting from October. *Planting
December	Brashing, pruning, cleaning
January	Fence and drain maintenance. Snow assists a check on rabbit or deer populations
February	Ground preparation, *planting broad-leaves (lowland sites)
March	Ground preparation, *planting
April	*Planting, beating up, harvesting; coppice-cutting up to April
May	*Weeding (as and when required to relieve competition)
June	–
July	Harvesting, control of woody weeds
August	Road construction or improvement

* Operations where timing is critical, depending on weather conditions and location.

jobs and if necessary can be spread out by dealing with small compartments in rotation rather than complete woods in one operation. This is better for landscape and wildlife, but a major constraint is the smallest size of load that can be economically transported (between 10 and 20 tonnes; see Chapter 4). Planting and weeding have to be done at specific times of the year, but the timing of most other operations can be more flexible (see Table 7.2). Work can often be done during the winter when there is likely to be less competition for labour, and when there will be least disturbance to the wildlife. Problems of labour scarcity can be resolved by co-operating with neighbours or alternatively by hiring a contractor.

Training

The staff employed should have the necessary training in forestry practices as mistakes can be very expensive and some operations are hazardous. Indeed, although existing labour may appear cheaper, lower skills and work rate may make them more expensive than contractors in the long run. Training is organised by the Forestry Training Council and the Agricultural Training Board.

Safety

Apart from training to improve professional competence in woodland management techniques, there is also a legal obligation for employers to provide adequate instruction, training and supervision to ensure, as far as is reasonably practicable, the health and safety at work of their employees (Health and Safety at Work, etc. Act, 1974). Health and safety extends to both the equipment the workers use and to the materials, especially pesticides, that they may handle (the Food and Environment Protection Act, 1985 and the Control of Pesticides Regulations, 1986).

Materials

The main materials that are required for woodland management are seeds or seedlings to plant, tree shelters or fencing for tree protection and herbicides for weed control.

Your choice of material for planting and how and at what distance you plant it will depend on the species concerned, the site conditions and your pocket. *Plants*

As a guide, Table 7.3 gives the approximate height and planting distances for young trees. The advantages and disadvantages of each are as follows.

1   **Transplants** are sturdy, 2–3-year-old plants with a large proportion of root in relation to shoot, giving them good powers of survival and growth especially in poor soils and on exposed sites. They will generally outgrow the more expensive standards in a few seasons and produce healthier and better formed trees and so are ideal for planting large areas. Protection is needed in the early years of growth from weed competition and from grazing animals.

2   Whips and **feathered trees** are well furnished with branches from low on the stem. They are more expensive and less sturdy than transplants but cheaper and easier to establish than standards, usually short enough not to require stakes and ties, but tall enough to prevent the leading shoots being damaged by hares, and easier to protect from rabbits than transplants. Weeding is less essential, but they will need protection from browsing animals.

3   Standards have a specified length of about 2 metres of clear stem below the first branches. They should be chosen only when individuals or small groups of trees are required or for avenues. They are less vulnerable to competition from weeds but more expensive and, being drought susceptible, more difficult to establish than transplants and whips. They require tree stakes, ties and protection from browsing animals.

Most trees are available either **bare-rooted, ball-rooted** ('root-wrapped'), or 'containerised'. Transplants, whips and feathered trees up to 90 centimetres high are usually delivered bare-rooted in bundles. Broad-leaved trees above this height are also usually moved bare-rooted, which tends to dry out the roots. To avoid this plants can be supplied root-wrapped, the roots being encased during transit in moist straw or other suitable material, held in place

Table 7.3   Height and planting distance of planting stock

Type	Overall height (metres)	Planting distance (metres)
Transplant	0.2–0.45	2
Whip	0.6–0.9	3–4
Whip or feathered whip	0.9–1.2	4
Feathered whip	1.5–1.8	4–5
Feathered whip	1.8–2.1	6
Light standard	2.5–2.75 (1.5–1.8 stem)	10+
Standard	2.75–3 (1.8 min. stem)	10+

(Source: Brooks, 1980)

with hessian. However, the plants must be handled carefully at all times to avoid overheating and physical damage and especially root drying. Sometimes a substantial proportion of young trees are dead when they are planted. Containerised plants are grown in a pot or cellular tray containing a balanced compost. They usually begin life under cover before being 'hardened off' outside. Some species (e.g. Corsican pine) are normally produced in paper pots for forest planting.

The advantage of containerised stock is that, as the roots are not exposed, they suffer little planting shock and initial survival can be higher. A disadvantage is that, where the ground being planted is heavy clay or very different in character from the growing compost, the roots of the young tree may be reluctant to penetrate the surrounding soil. Container-grown plants are also much more expensive than those supplied bare-rooted and, where a large area is to be planted, the weight of extra soil to be transported can cause problems. Conifers and evergreen shrubs over 90 centimetres high should never be bought without an earth ball lifted with the plant.

The planting method and the tools used are often a matter of preference, but they will also depend on site conditions. **Notch, screef, turf** or **mound, ridge** and **pit planting** techniques are all possible.

Some species, such as poplar and willow, root easily from cuttings and on suitable sites it may be possible to establish trees simply by taking cuttings from a parent tree and inserting them into slots in moist ground. This has the benefit of being cheap and conserves local planting stock.

Whatever type of planting stock is bought, it should be subject to the provisions of the European Community's Reproductive Material Regulations. These are designed to ensure that the origin of the seed from which plants have been raised meets specified standards and that such details are given to the purchaser.

Tree protection

Newly planted trees must be protected against animals.

Post and wire fencing will usually provide the most economic protection against large browsing animals where there are compact groups of trees or very large areas. Woven wire fencing should be used where there are sheep or other browsing animals. Protection against hares and rabbits can then be provided for existing fencing by adding chicken netting (width 105 centimetres, hexagonal mesh 3.1 centimetres, wire 0.125 centimetres thick) stapled to the fence, 15 centimetres of the bottom of the wire netting being bent back at right angles to the fence, on the side away from the trees, under the turf and soil. Ensure that rabbits are not fenced into the plantation. If rabbits cannot be excluded, tree guards may be more effective.

For large animals, electric fencing can be used, but this can involve high costs of inspection and maintenance, which are only really justified where you may want to move the fence fairly frequently.

On areas of less than 5 hectares, individual tree protection is normally cheaper than fencing (because 1 hectare requires roughly 400 metres of fencing or 400 metres per hectare, 4 hectares require 800 metres or 200 metres per hectare, and 16 hectares require only 1600 metres or 100 metres per hectare). Tree guards are made in a wide range of shapes, sizes and materials. All of them give a certain amount of protection against browsing animals, depending on their height. In addition, the polypropylene tubular shelters provide a micro-climate for the plant and some protection from weed competition. In some cases a

116

compromise is needed, using existing fencing where possible and protecting a few special trees with tubes, for example oak which would be the first to be eaten by rabbits.

Young trees must usually be kept clear of competing vegetation in their early years, particularly rank grasses in lowland areas and bracken and heather in the uplands.

There is a small range of herbicides approved for forestry use to control woody and non-woody weeds, usually applied with a knapsack sprayer. Herbicides are expensive and there is no need to treat more than 1 square metre of land around the tree to suppress the vegetation growth that would compete with it. Herbicides are also damaging to wildlife and human health if misused. They should not be used close to watercourses and the operator must have a recognised certificate of competence to apply pesticides as a contractor or if born after 31 December 1964 (unless working under direct supervision of a certificate holder). Furthermore, users of pesticides must comply with the conditions of approval relating to the use of specific products, which may cover situations where the treatment may be applied, the protective clothing required, the maximum dose rate and measures for the protection of wildlife and the environment. Thus, when selecting the application method the following points should be considered:

▶   the extent of the target area which needs to be controlled;

▶   the cost of the operation and any logistical problems together with the environmental and aesthetic impacts of the operation;

▶   the need to avoid damaging wildlife and other environmental interests through indiscriminate or careless application or disposal of containers and surplus herbicide.

Equipment

Clearing, brashing, pruning and coppicing small-sized material require relatively cheap, standard hand tools such as saws and hooks but larger work requires a chainsaw. For safety reasons it is better to buy an expensive, special purpose chainsaw rather than a general purpose one, and you must always wear all the necessary safety clothing.

Tractor-mounted mowers or brush cutters are most suitable for managing the non-woody and sometimes woody vegetation within glades and rides. Agricultural tractors and trailers can also be used for transporting materials, plants and small-sized produce. However, most farm tractors are not equipped to extract larger timber. Coppicing and felling small trees less than 7 centimetres in diameter can usually be done with hand tools. Although requiring less training than chainsaws, hand tools must still be used carefully, and unskilled staff need expert supervision. Note that coppice stools should always be cut with the cut face of the stem sloping away from the centre of the tree to prevent water collecting and encouraging rots.

Trees more than 7 centimetres in diameter are most likely to be felled with a chainsaw. The correct blade length for the size of the tree is important and a properly sharpened chain increases cutting speed. The felling direction should be worked out beforehand to make felling safe and extraction as simple as possible.

Chainsaw operators should never work alone, in case of an accident; help should always be on hand. Extraction methods, whether logs are to be carried out on trailers or dragged out of the wood, should be worked out in advance as well as the actual routes for extraction. Places are needed where timber can be stacked without interfering with either public roads or other hauliers' lorries. These are known as landings.

Legislation

Under TPOs, trees cannot be felled or branches cut without permission from the planning authority. Where permission is granted, replacement trees usually have to be planted.

A felling licence, granted by the Forestry Commission, is required to fell more than 5 cubic metres of timber (roughly equivalent to five mature trees) in any quarter of a year, of which not more than 2 cubic metres can be sold. A licence is not required for trees under 8 centimetres dbh; thinnings below 10 centimetres dbh; coppice below 15 centimetres dbh; trees in gardens, orchards, churchyards or public places; and dead or dangerous trees. As with TPOs the area affected usually has to be replanted.

Insurance and public safety

Where timber production is a priority for woodland, it is worth considering insurance against fire and storm damage. The risk from fire and wind varies with the type of wood (conifers are more likely to catch fire), location (heavy storms are more frequent in the north and west of Britain) and age (trees over 20 years of age are more prone to windthrow).

Third party cover is often very cheap and may be included in other schemes. This will be important in respect of safety with public access to woods. It is the responsibility of the manager and owner to assess tree health and, as far as possible, remove obviously dangerous trees or branches from public rights of way, car parks, nature trails and the like. Warning notices advising the public of unsafe trees or conditions, for example felling, do not absolve landowners from a duty to take reasonable care of the public in their woodland.

7.3   Monitoring

Both management plans and work plans are a statement of what the owner or manager would like to see happen to their woodland. For various reasons the work plan might not be fulfilled, for example staff are off sick at a critical time, or it may have an unexpected outcome, for example a large proportion of coppiced trees die after a very dry spring and need replacing. Such problems are always likely to happen but, as shown in the Atholl Estate's case study, a *problem* with red deer has been turned round to provide an *opportunity* to increase the conservation value of the area.

Having produced a management plan it will be easier to cope with unexpected events and adapt the plan to incorporate them. There is therefore a need to monitor developments, ranging from several times a year to every 5 years, to be able to recognise and act on any changes. Where timber production is important, regular checks of the health and state of the trees, especially in the early years, will be essential to ensure success (see Figure 7.1). If wildlife

Date	Rabbits seen	Deer seen	Holes in fence	Plant damage seen	Notes	Action taken	Signed
				DEER/RABBIT/FENCE REPORT ATHOLL ESTATE WOODLANDS CPT. NO. 36		VISITS REQUIRED Weekly	
6/12/88	Nil	5	One	A few trees browsed	General condition good	3 driven out Fence repaired 2 shot	D. Smith
14/12/88	Nil	Nil	Nil	No damage	✓	None	D. Smith
21/12/88	2	Nil	Nil Gate left open	A few trees damaged	✓	Rabbits shot Gate closed	D. Smith

conservation is a primary objective, annual surveys may be all that is required to monitor the gradual development or improvement of the woodland. Indeed, when grant aid is given, regular reviews of progress during and at the end of an approved period may be required as a condition of the grant, although monitoring should be seen as an enjoyable task rather than a burden.

Finally, the information from monitoring should feed directly into the management planning cycle (Figure 1.1), since woodland management plans should not be one-off tablets of stone but continually evolving records of achievement of the maintenance, enhancement and creation of valued landscapes and wildlife habitats.

Figure 7.1   Example of a monitoring form. This is one method of regularly checking fences for damage. It can be done by staff, a volunteer or someone paid a retainer to check, say, one plantation near their house

FURTHER READING

The following list includes books we recommend as further reading. Those marked with an asterisk were used as sources when writing this book.

*ADAS and Forestry Commission (1986) *Practical Work in Farm Woods No. 5. Woodland Management for Wildlife and Landscape Conservation.* P3021

*Andrews, J, Smart, N (1986) *Farm Woodlands and Birds.* RSPB, Sandy, Bedfordshire

*Blyth, J, Evans, J, Mutch, W E S, Sidwell, C (1987) *Farm Woodland Management.* Farming Press, Ipswich

*British Association of Shooting and Conservation (undated) *Woodlands for Shooting and Conservation.* BASC, Wrexham, Clwyd

*Brooks, A (1980) *Woodlands – a Practical Handbook.* BTCV, Wallingford, Oxfordshire

Cloudsley-Thompson, J L (1985) *British Naturalists' Association Guide to Woodlands.* The Crowood Press, Marlborough, Wiltshire

Coed Cymru (1987) *Making the Most of Your Farm Woods: Some Do's and Don'ts.* Coed Cymru, Newtown, Powys

*Evans, J (1984) *Silviculture of Broadleaved Woodland.* HMSO, London

*Forestry Commission (undated) Graphic techniques for forest design. Forestry Commission internal paper

*Forestry Commission (undated) Woodland planting on agricultural land: the implications for landscape and wildlife. Forestry Commission internal paper

Forestry Commission (undated) *Forests and Water: Guidelines.* Forestry Commission, Edinburgh

Forestry Commission (1989) *Forest Landscape Design Guidelines.* Forestry Commission, Edinburgh

Gair, R (1988) *Farm Conservation Guide.* Schering Agriculture, Nottingham

*Gray, N (1986) *Woodland Management for Pheasants and Wildlife.* David and Charles, Newton Abbot

Helliwell, D R (1988) *Economics of Woodland Management.* Packard Publishing, Chichester

*Hibberd, B G (ed) (1986) *Forestry Commission Bulletin No. 14: Forestry Practice.* HMSO, London

*Hibberd, B G (ed) (1988) *Forestry Commission Handbook No. 3: Farm Woodland Practice.* HMSO, London

Insley, H (ed) (1988) *Forestry Commission Bulletin No. 80: Farm Woodland Planning.* HMSO, London

Irving, J A (1985) *The Public in Your Woods.* Packard Publishing, Chichester

Joint Committee for the Conservation of British Insects (1986) Insect re-establishment – a code of conservation practice. *Antenna* 10(1), pp. 13–18

*Kirby, K J (1984) *Focus on Nature Conservation No. 8: Forestry Operations and Broadleaf Woodland Conservation.* Nature Conservancy Council, Peterborough

*Locke, G M L (1987) *Forestry Commission Bulletin No. 63: Census of Woodlands and Trees, 1979–82.* HMSO, London

McKelvie, C (1985) *A Future for Game?* George Allen and Unwin, London

MAFF (1984) *Farm Woodlands*, leaflet CL49. MAFF, Alnwick

*MAFF (1986) *Practical Work in Farm Woods*. MAFF, Alnwick

Mason, C, Long, S (1987) Management of lowland broadleaved woodland Bovingdon Hall, Essex. In: *Conservation Monitoring and Management*, CCP231, pp. 37–42. Countryside Commission, Cheltenham

Mitchell, A (1978) *A Field Guide to the Trees of Britain and Northern Europe* (2nd edn). Collins, London

*Morris, P (ed) (1980) *Natural History of the British Isles*. Country Life Books, Richmond, Surrey

Nature Conservancy Council (undated) *The Conservation of Butterflies*, leaflet E.26. NCC, Peterborough

Nature Conservancy Council (undated) *The Conservation of Semi-natural Upland Woodland*, leaflet 2.13. NCC, Peterborough

Nature Conservancy Council (undated) *The Conservation of Lowland Broadleaf Woodland*, leaflet 2.14. NCC, Peterborough

*Peterken, G (1985) *Woodland Conservation and Management*. Chapman and Hall, London

*Robertson, P A, Woodburn, M I A, Hill, D A (1988) The effects of woodland management for pheasants on the abundance of butterflies in Dorset, England. *Biological Conservation* 45, pp. 159–167

*Smart, N, Andrews, J (1985) *Birds and Broadleaves Handbook*. RSPB, Sandy

*Soutar, R G, Peterken, G F (1989) Regional lists of native trees and shrubs for use in afforestation schemes. *Arboricultural Journal* 13, pp. 33–43

*TGUK (1985) *The Forestry and Woodland Code*. Timber Growers United Kingdom, London

The Woodland Trust (1986) *Community Woodland Resource Pack*. The Woodland Trust, Grantham

Forest Industry Safety Guides

The Safety Guides published by the Forestry Safety Council give a summary of safe working practices, helping employees and employers to comply with the Health and Safety at Work, etc. Act, 1974. In many cases, an apppropriate checklist is available for use by supervisors, safety officers, etc. at inspections. All are available free from the Forestry Safety Council at the following address:

The Secretary, Forestry Safety Council, 231 Corstorphine Road, Edinburgh EH12 7AT.

GLOSSARY

Afforestation The planting of trees on previously unwooded land.

Agroforestry A system producing both forestry and agricultural (animal or plant) crops in an intimate mixture from the same land.

Ancient woodland Woodland that has existed continuously on the site since AD 1600.

Ball-rooted tree Tree transplanted with the earth around its roots intact.

Bare-rooted tree Tree lifted for transplanting without earth around its roots.

Beating up Replacement of failures in a newly planted tree crop (normally done at yearly intervals after planting), also known as filling up.

Biomass The weight of all the organisms forming a given population or trophic level or inhabiting a given region.

Bole The stem or trunk of a tree.

Brash(n) Small branches trimmed from the sides and top of a main stem. Also known as lop and top and as slash.

Brash(v) To prune away all branches from the lower trunk (normally up to 2 or 3 metres) of plantation-grown trees.

Butt Bottom end (root end) of a log or pole.

Canopy The uppermost layer of woodland structure. Usually 8–30 metres above ground. Contains the standard, emergent and understorey trees.

Cleaning Removal of unwanted woody species (which have usually arrived by natural regeneration or have regrown from cut stumps) from amongst young crop trees.

Clear felling Complete removal of the whole tree crop at one time.

Climax community The end point of an undisturbed succession under the prevailing climatic and soil conditions.

Compartment A section of woodland managed as one block.

Coniferous Woodland comprising cone-bearing trees, e.g. firs, pines.

Coppice(n)(*copse*) Woodland consisting of stools of broad-leaved trees that gives rise to successive crops of poles and sticks when cut on a rotation.

Coppice(v)
1   To fell trees close to the ground with the intention of producing coppice shoots from the stools.
2   To produce coppice shoots.
3   To harvest the coppice shoots as a crop of poles and stakes.

Coupe A coppice plot cut on a regular basis or a clear felled area in a plantation. Also known as a panel.

Covert A small wood, usually in the midst of farmland, managed primarily for game.

Crown The spreading branches and foliage of a tree.

Crown thinning See thinning.

Cutting A small section of young shoot or root used to propagate a new plant.

dbh (diameter at breast height) The mean diameter of trees measured 1.3 metres above ground level.

Deciduous Woodland and trees that shed leaves in the autumn.

Dedication Scheme A scheme introduced in 1946 to encourage rehabilitation for timber production of wartime fellings. Discontinued in 1974.

Epicormic shoots A secondary growth from dormant or adventitious buds on the stem or main branches. Should not be confused with suckers.

Epiphyte A plant attached to another plant but not parasitic on it, e.g. lichens.

Feathered tree A young tree well furnished with branches to near ground level.

Field layer That part of the woodland structure containing herbaceous plants and undershrubs. Usually about 10 centimetres to 2 metres above ground level.

Forest An area of heavily wooded land. In the past a tract of land, not necessarily wooded, controlled by the Crown – originally for large game – and administered according to special rules.

Forestry The management of forest plantations to produce timber.

Forwarder A trailer system where sawlogs are carried fully suspended on the trailer.

Glade A clearing or open place in a forest or woodland.

Ground layer That part of the woodland structure, up to about 10 centimetres above ground, containing mosses, herbs and the seedlings of plants of the higher layers.

Hardwood The timber of any broad-leaved tree whether actually hard or not.

High forest A forest consisting of maiden trees allowed to reach full height with a closed and high canopy.

Layer A side shoot which roots to form a new but connected plant where it touches the ground.

Leader The main top shoot of a tree.

Line thinning See thinning.

Lop and top See brash.

Low thinning See thinning.

Maiden A young seedling tree which has not been cut back.

Mound planting Planting a tree with its roots in a mound of earth thrown up to ensure good aeration, free drainage and less competition. This technique is often used on wet ground by turning over turves into which a tree is notch planted or more usually by spreading out dollops of soil/peat with a back-hoe or excavator.

Natural regeneration Regeneration of woodland through naturally occurring seedlings.

Notch planting Planting in a conical hole made by a dibber or in a slit in the ground in a 'T', 'H' or 'L' shape made with a spade. Unsuitable for large trees or in wet soil.

Nurse crop A crop of trees grown to encourage the growth of another species by protecting the latter from, for example, wind, frost or strong sunlight.

Park Originally, land enclosed for the keeping of semi-wild animals. Later, an area enclosed for amenity.

pH A measure of acidity and alkalinity on a scale from 0 to 14.0; pH 7 is neutral, less than 7 is acid and more than 7 is alkaline. In soils a pH of 4.5 and below is regarded as extremely acid, pH 6.6–7.3 as neutral and a pH over 9 as very strongly alkaline.

Pit planting Planting in a pit of prepared or cultivated soil. Essential for trees over 90 centimetres tall and also worthwhile when beating up.

Plantation An area of woodland where most of the trees have been planted for timber.

Pole stage A stage in the growth of young trees at which the crowns are above head height but the timber taken out in thinnings, etc., is below the size of saw timber.

Pollard(n) A tree cut at 2–4 metres above ground level, then allowed to grow again to produce a crop of branches.

Pollard(v) To cut the branches from a pollarded tree so that they will regrow.

Primary woodland Woodland that has had a continuous cover of native trees throughout history.

Provenance The place of origin of a tree stock, which remains the same no matter where later generations of the trees are raised.

Pruning The removal of live branches from the stem so that subsequent growth produces a cylinder of knot-free timber around a knotty stem core. Pruning is usually confined to the main crop trees to produce quality timber.

Pulpwood A timber which is destined to be used for the production of wood pulp (for paper or board manufacture). Generally small roundwood in 2 or 3 metre lengths.

Recent woodland Woodland which has grown up since AD 1600.

Ride A pathway or track in woodland.

Ridge planting Planting in a notch on a ridge made by ploughing.

Rotation Length of time between successive fellings of a plantation or cuttings of a coppice plot.

Roundwood Small diameter timber which is usually too small to be sawn and is used for poles, stakes, pulp or chipwood.

Sawlogs Timber of a size and quality suitable for conversion in a saw mill, e.g. a large straight log, bole or branch.

Scarify Scratching or disturbing the soil surface.

Screef planting Planting in a notch made after the turf is removed to expose the soil and reduce weed competition.

Scrub In ecology, an area dominated by shrubs, possibly as a stage in succession to high forest. In forestry, an area of unproductive woodland.

Secondary woodland Woodland growing on a site that has been cleared at some time.

Semi-natural woodland On ancient sites, woods made up mainly of native species growing where their presence is apparently natural and which have not obviously been planted. On recent sites, all stands that have originated mainly by natural regeneration.

Shake Cracking of timber due to stresses of growth, impact of felling or drying.

Shrub layer That part of the woodland structure, from about 2–4.5 metres above ground containing shrubs and young growth of canopy trees.

Silviculture The growing and tending of trees in woodlands, plantations or natural forests.

Singled Reduced to a single stem. Usually applied to coppice stools where several stems may be cut off to leave just one stem to grow on.

Site of Special Scientific Interest (SSSI) Area designated by the NCC as of special interest, because of its flora, fauna, geology or physiography, outside nature reserves.

Skidder A tractor used to extract timber from the stump to the ride or roadside by dragging (skidding) all or part of the load along the ground.

Snedding The removal of branches from a felled tree.

Softwood Timber derived from, or alternative name for, coniferous trees, irrespective of actual hardness.

Stand A group of trees, often applied to groups of trees of the same age.

Standards
1   Widely spaced trees left to grow on to maturity often with coppice or a successor generation growing under and between them.
2   Transplanted trees with an upright clean stem supporting a head. Plants in standard form are described, in descending order according to the height of the clear stem, as tall standard, standard and half standard.
3   In woodland structure trees forming the dominant layer of the canopy.

Stool The stump or cut base of a shrub or tree from which new shoots grow. See also coppice.

Structure The pattern of woodland and habitat elements such as the height and density of crowns, position and size of glades and shape and orientation of margins.

Sucker Woody shoots arising from an underground stem or root, or shoots arising from the understock of a worked (grafted or budded) plant.

Sun scorch Damage caused to bark by unaccustomed exposure to the sun, for example, after the sudden removal of shade.

Thicket stage Stage after planting and before the pole stage in the growth of a plantation or natural regeneration during which the lower branches of the growing trees meet and interlace.

Thinning The removal, at certain stages of growth, of a proportion of trees from a crop; for example, to allow the remainder more growing space or to obtain a supply of timber.

1   *Crown thinning* Removal of neighbouring trees which are interfering with the development of the best crowns in the crop.

2   *Line thinning* Removal of complete rows of trees, often used initially as an alternative to brashing as a way of gaining access to a crop.

3   *Low thinning* Individual selection and marking of the trees to be removed.

Transplant Any plant which has been transplanted one or more times in the nursery. This is done to develop a better root:shoot ratio than would be the case if the trees were allowed to grow undisturbed from the time of sowing to the time when they are planted out in the wood.

Tree shelter Plastic tubes placed around newly planted trees to encourage fast early growth and to offer some protection from mammals and chemical sprays.

Trunk The living stem of a shrub or tree.

Turf planting See mound planting.

Understorey Layer of trees with crowns below those of the dominant trees in the canopy.

Underwood

1   The lower storey in a high forest, often coppice being grown under standards.

2   Cut wood of coppice poles, young suckers or (less often) pollard poles.

Whip A young tree consisting only of a single slender stem, usually of one or two year's growth.

Wilding A naturally occurring seedling.

Windblow See windthrow.

Windthrow Blowing down of trees by the wind. Also known as windblow.

Wolf tree A large, quick-growing but coarsely and poorly formed tree of low timber quality.

Woodland An area mainly covered by trees.

Wood-pasture Woodland in which grazing or browsing has been the dominant influence.

Acknowledgements

The Open University course team is greatly indebted to the many people, with a wide range of experience of countryside management, who have contributed to the development of this teaching programme.

First, we must acknowledge the very generous financial support of the Nature Conservancy Council, along with the Esmée Fairbairn Charitable Trust and the Ernest Cook Trust.

We also value the comments and the support of the external assessor, Professor Bryn Green, The Sir Cyril Kleinwort Professor of Countryside Management, Wye College, University of London.

Thirdly, we are extremely grateful to the two consultants who helped with the case studies and other material: C Langton (Forest Manager for the Atholl Estates) and D Whelon (Sussex Conservation Adviser, Farming and Wildlife Advisory Group).

Finally, we would like to thank the many other people who provided source material for the book or read and commented on preliminary drafts:

K Bayes (Royal Society for the Protection of Birds)
S Bell (Forestry Commission)
R Carmichael (Dyfed County Council)
F Curry (Forestry Commission)
P Gilder (Countryside Commission)
E Hamilton (Woodland Trust)
E Hammond (Nature Conservancy Council)
S Hodgson (British Trust for Conservation Volunteers)
S Humphreys (Silvanus)
G Kerby (Agricultural Training Board)
K Kirby (Nature Conservancy Council)
R MacMullen (Farming and Wildlife Advisory Group)
G Peterken (Nature Conservancy Council)
P Robertson (Game Conservancy)
R Robinson (Nature Conservancy Council, Scotland)
D Saunders (East Sussex Small Woodlands Project)
A Sayers (Timber Growers United Kingdom)
J Webb (Coed Cymru)

Grateful acknowledgement is made to the following sources for permission to use material in this book:

Figures
Figures 3.1 and 3.2: from P. Morris, *Natural History of the British Isles*, 1980, Midsummer Books Ltd. Reprinted by permission of Hamlyn Publishing Group; *Figures 6.5 and 6.7*: from *Woodlands for Shooting and Conservation*, 1987, British Association for Shooting and Conservation.

Tables
Tables 4.2, 5.1 and 5.2: modified by permission from J. Evans, *Silviculture of Broadleaved Woodland*, 1984, Forestry Commission. Reproduced with the permission of the Controller of Her Majesty's Stationery Office; *Tables 4.1, 4.3, 4.4, 4.5 and 7.1*: modified by permission from *Practical Work in Farm Woods*, 1986, Ministry of Agriculture, Fisheries and Food. Reproduced with the permission of the Controller of Her Majesty's Stationery Office; *Tables 5.3 and 5.5*: modified by permission from N. Stuart and J. Adams, *Birds and Broadlands Handbook*, 1985, Royal Society for the Protection of Birds; *Table 6.2*: from *Woodlands for Shooting and Conservation*, 1987, British Association for Shooting and Conservation; *Table 7.2*: modified by permission from *Woodlands*, 1987, British Trust for Conservation Volunteers.

Index

A

access: for harvesting 56–7;
  public 61–2, 88–90
afforestation 8
agroforestry 51, 58
alder 38, 55, 99
ancient monuments 20
ancient woodland 20, 33, 39–
  40, 43
Ancient Woodland
  Inventory 28, 33
archaeological features 20
Area of Outstanding Natural
  Beauty 21
ash 38, 55, 99, 102
assessment: of commercial
  value 51–72; of habitat 32,
  50; of landscape 16–31
Atholl Estate see case studies
attitude of owner see owner

B

beating up 76
beech 7, 31, 37; age/
  diameter 55; estimated
  national area 38; ideal site
  conditions 99; wildlife
  value 102
birch 32, 38, 55, 99, 102
birds 44, 85–7
brashing 54
broad-leaved trees 76 see also
  native species and individual
  types e.g. oak
broad-leaved woodland 28, 30–
  1, 32, 79 see also deciduous
  woodland
butterflies 84, 85

C

canopy, tree 9–10
case studies: Atholl Estate:
  background 14; business
  assessment 66–8; deer-
  damage 108–9; habitat
  assessment 47–8; landscape
  assessment 22–7;
  management
  compartments 51–2;
  management options 108–9;
  wood-pasture 58:
  small woods in Sussex:
  background 15; business
  assessment 68–72; habitat
  assessment 48–50; landscape
  assessment 28–31;

management options 109–11
checklists: habitat
  assessment 40, 47, 50;
  landscape features 26
cherry 55, 99, 103
cleaning stage 54, 78
clear felling 79
climate 34
climax community 32
commercial sites see timber
  production
commercial value,
  assessment 51–72
compartments 51–2
coniferous woodland 55, 76,
  79; ecosystem 36 see also case
  studies (Atholl Estate) and non-
  native species
container-grown trees 116
contractors 57
coppice 10, 11, 80;
  overgrown 43;
  restoration 74–5;
  terminology and types 81
copse 31
costs, management 113–18

D

damage 89; by deer 15, 68,
  108–9
dbh see diameter at breast height
deciduous woodland 34, 37;
  ecosystem 35 see also broad-
  leaved woodland and individual
  species e.g. oak
Dedication Scheme 14, 66
deer: damage 15, 68, 108–9;
  management 61, 107
density of planting 54, 55, 56;
  young trees 115
diameter at breast height
  (dbh) 54, 55; estimating tree
  volume from 57;
  specifications for end-uses 56
disease 55
diversity: of species 41, 76;
  structural 19, 41–3
dominant species 12
drainage 101

E

ecological processes 34–9
elder 10, 99
elm 38, 99
Enclosure, Acts of 51

Environmentally Sensitive
  Area 15, 111
equipment 117–18
expert advice 44, 55, 62, 71
extraction methods 56, 117–18

F

feathered trees and whips 115
felling: licence 118;
  patterns 96, 97; stage 54,
  78–80
fencing 116
field layer 9, 10
firewood 51, 53, 56
flushing areas (pheasants) 105–
  6
food webs 35, 36, 37
Forestry Commission 58, 118

G

game conservancy 107
game management 60–1;
  designing woodland for 102–
  7; siting of coverts 93, 104
glades 84
grant aid 112
grassland 92
grazing 43, 58
ground layer 9, 10
group felling 79

H

habitat, assessment 32–50
harvesting 56–7
hazel 38, 99, 103
health and safety 114
heathland 92
hedges 92
herbicides 117
high forest 10, 11, 12, 43
hornbeam 38, 99

I

indicator species 44
insects 84–5
insurance 118
introduced species 33

K

Killiehangie Hill see case studies
  (Atholl Estate)

L

labour requirements 113–14
landform, types 26